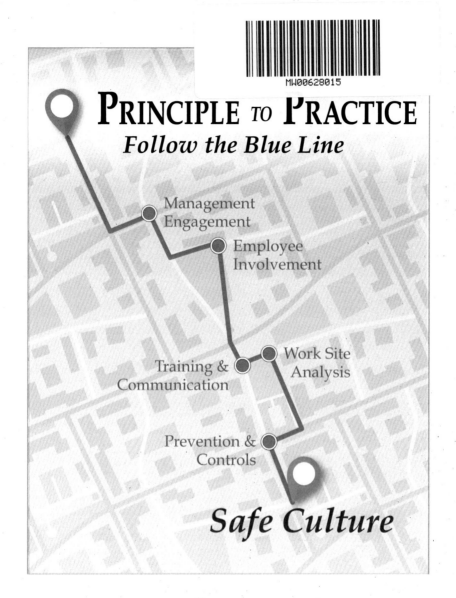

PRINCIPLE *TO* PRACTICE
Follow the Blue Line

Management Engagement

Employee Involvement

Training & Communication

Work Site Analysis

Prevention & Controls

Safe Culture

DAVID G. LYNN, CSP

PEAK SAFETY PERFORMANCE

MW00628015

Copyright © 2020 by David G. Lynn, CSP

Published by PEAK Safety Performance™

No part of this book may be used or reproduced in any manner whatsoever without written permission, except in the case of brief quotations embedded in critical articles and reviews.

ISBN: 978-0-9981102-3-3

Produced by:
Great Life Press
Rye, New Hampshire
greatlifepress.com

for

PEAK Safety Performance™
Seneca, South Carolina
peaksafetyperformance.com

Contents

Books by David G. Lynn, CSP

Strategic Safety Plan
Overview: Learn how to build your safety framework in
simple steps.

HANDS ON Safety Champion Program
Overview: Develop a strategic plan to reduce hand injuries
with employee involvement.

Safety Champion Program
Overview: Encourage employee involvement with focused
safety audits.

CONTEXT Root Cause Analysis Handbook
Overview: Collect and analyze facts in a systematic way so
that you can influence the future.

Safety Walkthrough Guide
Overview: Utilize this pocket guide for quick answers about
safety requirements.

Safety Talking Points
Overview: Deliver great safety toolbox topics utilizing
standard safety talking points.

Principle To Practice
Overview: Learn how to implement proven safety principles
with effective practices.

Peak Safety Orientation Handbook
Overview: Distribute a standard safety orientation
handbook with basic safety requirements.

To order copies, visit https://peaksafetyperformance.com

Acknowledgments

The inspiration to create a book comes from many perspectives, but the most important element I want to recognize is the desire to communicate lessons learned based on real examples and personal experience. My goal is to help readers take their next steps in building a successful safety culture by learning from my failures and my successes.

My approach in this book is driven by the following core values that I hope you can see throughout the book.

1. **Stay Grounded.** I believe that faith influences our decisions both at home and at work. I strive to stay grounded in my Christian roots, which ultimately governs the way I do business.

2. **Maintain Balance.** There is no success in business worth failure at home. I work hard to balance both work and family expectations.

3. **Finish First.** People remember who finishes first. I strive to be the first to learn, first to achieve, first to respond, first to act, and first to remain humble in the process.

4. **Over-Deliver.** I want to meet and exceed all client expectations through every service I provide.

5. **Focus on Strengths.** I want to be great at a few things rather than average in many things.

6. **Do What You Can, When You Can.** I want to check it off the list as soon as possible and gain momentum with progress.

7. **Enjoy the Trip as Much as the Destination.** I love the work involved with achievement just as much as the reward itself.

Safety is serious business and I want to communicate safety principles with a personal touch and a sense of purpose. I hope my light-hearted approach to convey important messages will influence readers to apply these ideas in their environments.

I want to thank Brad Dunker for reviewing the material and offering his words of wisdom in the Foreword. His positive approach to my request has been is an encouragement. He took the time to labor through the material, and he added incredible value to the project. I would also like to thank Susan Dunlap for her technical editing contribution. She helped make the book worth reading. And I would like to thank Grace Peirce for her work on yet another project. She is a huge help and I am grateful for her contribution. Thank you all!

My family has also provided unique inspiration that can be found in the analogies throughout the book. My boys Caleb, Jacob, and Luke offer a wealth of material to make safety relevant to a working environment. They teach me to look for critical safety messages in simple life experiences. I also want to recognize my wife Lisa. Her never-ending support made it possible to compile this work.

Some say that there is nothing new under the sun, but I think that there *is* always a unique experience in everyone's life that has the potential to impact another life. Our job is to share what we have seen, heard, and experienced, and I want to encourage readers to look for ways to improve the quality of life of those around them with their influence.

I also want to thank God for the influence He has had in my life and I want to thank Him for the opportunities He has given me that have inspired this book.

Foreword

I graduated from college and started working in the Health, Safety, and Environmental (HSE) field as a specialist for the Air Force. An Air Force base was not a place that I ever imagined I would end up, living on the bare necessities and government pay. Over the next 31 years, I advanced in my career, and I am now working in an Executive HSE Director role for the Fluor® Corporation (an Engineering, Construction, Procurement, and Fabrication company). In a roller coaster sort of way, my challenges have been great, including financial ups and downs, multiple moves and geographical changes, and bosses who were just plain tough. However, during my career I also met some awesome people, especially within the last couple of decades.

When David Lynn was hired on with Fluor, I had a different perception of him than the rest of the safety managers. I have always been terrible about first impressions, and I missed the boat on David as well. He seemed very intelligent and job-focused, but I had already made up my mind that we were not going to be close colleagues, and certainly not friends. Boy, was I wrong! As I got to know David, he became a great friend of mine. Today, I categorize him as one of the most intelligent, focused, and driven men I have ever met in HSE. His desire to help others is unmatchable. His organized style, his intelligence, and his drive make his coworkers better at their professions. While I have come to know David as a former colleague and as a current friend, the other connection David and I share is our faith. I believe that his Christian background and his exemplary standards make up his success. David puts his family first, and aligns his work and faith to ensure that his direction has solid ground.

In this book, *Principle to Practice: Follow the Blue Line*, David has put together an excellent explanation of how a company can take safety to a higher level. Many companies struggle to barely meet the minimum standards of safety compliance. In this book, David pushes beyond the basic safety requirements. He draws on his experiences to create "Leadership-Based" actions that will drive the safety culture of an organization. Some key points that stood out to me in this book speak about the vital nature of the "Quality" of your program elements, and the important fact that "Leadership Visible Engagement" is a must.

Quality is the basic fiber of anything we do. We can do a lot of things, but if our actions have no quality, they will not last. What David is teaching us is like either buying a cheap product, or buying a more expensive version of the product – but made with quality. The products may look the same, but the quality product lasts longer and holds its value, just like a quality safety program. For all of us in HSE, that investment is paramount. In explaining the importance of leadership, David drives home the critical point that leaders must "lead." Our company leaders must be committed, they must be engaged, and they must build positive relationships with their workforce. In this book, David clearly explains how to build the culture of safety required for your organization or project.

I believe that this book is a great guide for any company that is looking to enhance their safety program and get their leadership engaged. David has professionally laid out the key attributes for what it will take for your company to step up to a higher level of safety. From "Management Commitment and Engagement" to "Key Training Elements," all the information presented can make your program successful, if applied correctly. I should know, as I have used David's methods and seen the success.

Brad Dunker, CSP
Executive HSE Director for the Fluor Corporation

Prologue

I graduated from Furman University in Greenville, South Carolina, with a Bachelor of Arts degree in Health and Physical Education. I planned to coach football. You are probably asking yourself, "How did he end up with a career in safety?" I can assure you that my career path was not intentional.

When I graduated, I realized that I loved sports but I did not want to teach. I was scared to speak in front of people. (Isn't that ironic?) This unproductive combination did not give me many options, so I had to expand my job search. I applied for jobs in industries such as construction, manufacturing, sales, and the government. I was willing to work anywhere that would give me a chance.

I applied for a job as a Compliance Officer with OSHA. I did not know what OSHA did, but they were hiring and I needed a job. I did a little research and I came to the conclusion that they were the "Safety Police." I thought to myself, "I can do that." I was blessed with the opportunity to interview with the Director of OSHA in South Carolina, and he offered me a job.

I used to think my introduction to the safety profession was odd because it was so random. But I have discovered that we all have our own story. Every safety professional has a unique origin, and we all have our "first" introduction to safety. The key is to build on every experience and make your impact count.

My journey in the safety field began in 1992 working as a Compliance Officer. I led safety inspections and fatality investigations across a variety of industries. The regulatory background exposed me to successful safety cultures, as well as cultures that did not demonstrate a commitment to safety. This well-rounded experience provided me with a unique perspective on how to build a world-class safety culture. The first three years of my career laid a foundation for my occupation.

Three years into my OSHA job, I realized that the opportunities in my profession were endless. Duracell® gave me an opportunity to lead safety in a fast-paced manufacturing environment as an Environmental, Health, and Safety Engineer. The facility had a dynamic environment with unique hazards. They manufactured AA & AAA batteries for North America. I spent five years learning how to apply what I learned at OSHA in the Duracell organization.

In 2000, I started work for Owens Corning as an Environmental, Health, and Safety Manager during the company's construction phase of a state-of-the-art manufacturing facility. I managed construction health and safety activities and I coordinated environmental permitting processes for the project. I was instrumental in the commissioning phases of the plant, while I remained as the Environmental, Health, and Safety Manager for the plant, until 2004.

I leveraged my diverse background and started work with the Fluor Corporation in 2004. Fluor has a distinguished safety reputation, and they are recognized as being one of the world's safest companies. At Fluor, I served as a U.S. Regional HSE Manager, Senior Corporate Programs Manager, Global HSE Director for Upstream Chemicals, and Global Deputy Director for Energy & Chemicals. In these roles, I led teams responsible for global training, auditing, workers' compensation, substance abuse, regulatory compliance, communications, and high impact corporate programs such as OSHA's Voluntary Protection Program (VPP). I provided HSE oversight and support for multi-billion dollar "mega" projects in challenging environments.

After working in the corporate environment at Fluor for eight years, I decided to continue my career by becoming a consultant. In a consultant role, I help clients solve problems and achieve their goals using a Principle to Practice philosophy. My company, Peak Safety Performance, LLC, utilizes the concepts in my book to help clients build exceptional safety cultures. Peak Safety Performance delivers a variety of Safety Transformation Workshops and Safety Leadership Classes.

Introduction
Setting Your Sights on Results-Based Safety Leadership

Most corporations claim to have safety as a value, but few companies deliver world-class safety performance. When I worked with OSHA as a compliance officer, company representatives would share with me what they "believed" about safety.

I heard common values such as, "Safety is a condition of employment," "Safety is everyone's responsibility," and "Training is essential to injury prevention and NO injury is acceptable!" Does all that sound familiar? Most companies have their version of these similar guiding principles.

Yet if most companies claim the same fundamental principles, why is there such a disparity in safety performance? Simple: Some companies lack the right safety character, mentality, and drive to achieve positive results. As an OSHA compliance officer, I observed companies with a comprehensive knowledge of fundamental safety concepts that did not (or could not) balance their intellectual safety knowledge with a "boots on the ground" reality. Conceptual safety is worthless without the ability to produce positive results.

Safety Character

My favorite quotes about character come from Coach John Wooden. He said, "Be more concerned with your character than your reputation, because your character is what you really are, while your reputation is merely what others think you are."

Wooden also said, "Ability may get you to the top, but it takes character to keep you there."

These statements amplify the importance of a fundamental value system that defines your organization and guides you through difficult decisions. Safety character is the pulse of your culture, and it sustains your success. The following three characteristics are a great start to help build character in your program.

Commitment: Commitment is a not a casual attribute. To meet high expectations, commitment requires sacrifice. It is a dedication to your safety goals and it is a relentless pursuit of zero accidents. To realize the truest sense of the word "commitment," you have to demonstrate the characteristic with consistency and visibility. Words are meaningless; actions are everything.

Discipline: Discipline compliments commitment, and it minimizes uncertainty in your culture. When employees see safety discipline in your organization, they clearly understand where the lines are, and the structured climate influences people to make safe decisions. There is no question about how, when, where, and why safety is important. Discipline elevates each employee's expectation to achieve success.

Urgency: *Webster's Dictionary* defines urgency as:

1) Compelling immediate action; 2) Urging; pressing; besetting; plying, with importunity; calling for immediate attention; instantly important; 3) Being imperative, exigent or imperious; 4) Being instant or immediate; 5) Being important, earnest, serious or weighty; 6) Being critical or crucial.

In the context of safety character, leaders have to convey a sense of urgency about safety that mirrors the dictionary definition. Safety calls for immediate action. Urgency with safety should feel like your team is fourth and inches from the goal line, determined to score. Injury prevention is the play that scores the touchdown.

These three safety character traits are not all inclusive, but they will help you build a foundation that will contribute to positive results. The question is: Would your coworkers say you demonstrate these characteristics?

Safety Attributes & Character			
Urgent	Disciplined	Accountable	Ethical
People-Oriented	High Expectations	Organized	Systematic
Consistent	Visible	Enthusiastic	Committed

The Right Safety Leader Mentality

When I refer to a safety leader, I am not talking about the guy that holds the "safety man" title. I am talking about operational leaders, managers, and line supervisors who influence behavior. They drive results in their areas of responsibility. All leaders have to manage work with a visible commitment to each employee's safety.

The right safety leader responds to their circumstances with an unwavering and unquestionable commitment to do things safely. There is no room for compromise.

Results-based safety leaders have a distinct mentality and attitude that demonstrate that they are determined to succeed. They think like winners. They take responsibility, and they drive achievements. They are not passive. They demonstrate the mentality described in the table below. Commitment, discipline, and urgency complement the right safety leader's mentality.

Results-Based Safety Mentality			
1	Focus relentlessly on "leading indicator" goals.	6	Experiment and innovate to improve safety.
2	Take complete responsibility for the group's safety results.	7	Measure the right safety standards with increasing rigor.
3	Do not make excuses or explain away the results.	8	Constantly take action.
4	Communicate expectations consistently and clearly.	9	Seek improvement feedback from others.
5	Do something personally to improve the safety results.	10	Model the methods you want your group to put into practice.

Top 10 Desired Safety Results

A game plan gives you the insight to win, but you cannot know who won without a score. You do not know how your players performed unless you keep statistics. A strategic system to evaluate people with clear and quantifiable measures will instill accountability.

As a leader with the right safety mentality, you have to fight against the inclination to define safety results in ambiguous terms. My three sons – Caleb, Jacob, and Luke – provide a practical example of ambiguous results. If I ask them how they are doing in school, what response do you think I get? They communicate in one-word sentences: good, fine, OK. What does that tell me? If I want to know how they performed in school, I have to look at their work. Every test has a score; every project has a grade. The rewards and consequences for grades motivate my boys to perform, and I cannot accept general descriptions.

Weak safety cultures define their results with vague measures. They cannot identify their weak performers, because they do not quantify their safety engagement.

When I worked with OSHA, I often found inadequate

descriptions of safety performance. When I asked employers to describe their safety performance, some people responded with vague answers: fine, OK, good. Strong safety cultures avoid these traps. They keep score of critical leading indicators, and they demand visible management participation. When you ask someone in a strong safety culture about the facility's performance, he or she will define the facility's status in clear measurements. The Safety Manager knows the weak and strong leaders because their contributions are quantified.

For example, if audits are required, track audit participation and measure the quality of the audits. If an organization values sustained corrective action, track the number of repeat observations for each audit. If a program requires supervisors to perform prejob briefs (PJB), track the quality and participation in the PJB process. The records become a results-based performance measurement.

True accountability means that you find the right motivation to drive your desired results. This is a perfect opportunity to instill expectations, urgency, and discipline into your program.

So what do you hope to gain? What is the desired outcome? Where do you start? The table below provides food for thought. Measure the visibility and participation of your leaders.

The key question is, "What quantifiable results do you want?"

Top 10 Desired Safety Results			
1	Set and achieve aggressive improvement goals for injury rates.	6	Schedule, track, and monitor manager participation in orientations.
2	Perform a minimum of one audit per week per manager and supervisor.	7	Schedule and deliver ALL required training with manager visibility.
3	Achieve aggressive improvement goals with scored audits.	8	Attend a minimum of one safety meeting per week. (ALL employees)
4	Track and monitor manager participation in investigations.	9	Conduct a minimum of one safety performance review a week.
5	Track and monitor daily manager participation in prejob briefs.	10	Track and monitor response time for corrective actions.

The right safety character and mentality fuels the engine to deliver results, but every organization has to define and communicate what they want to achieve. You have to balance your intellectual understanding of safety with a "boots on the ground" reality. Conceptual safety is worthless without the ability to motivate and produce results. Does your organization have the right balance?

This book describes the general processes, procedures, practices, and techniques that will help your company execute exceptional safety performance with the right safety character, mentality, and desired results. The purpose of this strategic plan is to implement proven principles and practices that will build an exceptional safety culture. This plan identifies strategies that companies can use to execute strategic safety requirements that will drive peak safety performance.

— First published in *EHS Today*, by David G. Lynn, CSP, July 09, 2012

PRINCIPLE 1
Management Commitment and Engagement

Average safety performance is not hard to achieve, and many companies are satisfied to coast to mediocre results. Company leaders have to commit their efforts to attain exceptional safety performance. One of the first steps to transform your company's safety culture to "best in class" is to adopt a "Best is Standard" mentality. To achieve this goal, it takes 100% management commitment, participation, and engagement in leading indicator processes that drive the result.

Visible management commitment does not happen by accident. Company leaders have to establish a strategic plan with clear goals for management participation and engagement in the safety process. The plan should include ways to quantify expectations and hold leaders accountable. Keep score! The scorecard for individual contributors will drive improvement and instill accountability in the workplace. A score provides a method to integrate urgency into an individual's daily expectations. A scorecard differentiates the best from the worst.

When I worked with OSHA as a compliance officer in the early nineties, I inspected more than 200 companies. When I asked company leaders to describe their safety performance, they provided vague responses: fine, OK, good. Superficial descriptions of safety performance are common because we do not always measure the detailed leading indicators that promote success. Strong safety cultures avoid these traps. They keep score on critical leading indicators, and they take an active interest in the details.

If your organization does not keep detailed individual scores for safety, you will experience an adjustment period when you introduce the idea. I learned this lesson the hard way. When I worked at Owens Corning, I developed a scorecard that tracked management participation in four categories. I tracked audit participation, safety team support, safety meeting completion, and safety procedure reviews. Each supervisor and manager had responsibilities, and I documented their performance. I gave them a score for each item, and I rolled up the scores into a final score. Then I stack-ranked each leader from the best to the worst. I highlighted the top 10% in green and the bottom 10% in red.

After the report was complete, I distributed the report to the leadership team. The process sounds reasonable, right? The score showed who followed through with their responsibilities and who did not. That level of data analysis is the type of accountability you need because it tells you who deserves a reward and who needs motivation. After all, safety is a condition of employment. You have to know the score, and the score has to mean something.

The problem I encountered was my manager was in the red! How do you hide your boss's performance? The system was valuable because it measured management commitment with visible tools that are proven to drive safety success. No one could hide behind vague performance answers like good, fine, and OK. However, the backlash can be dangerous. When my manager reviewed the results, he came to my office in a bad mood. Needless to say, he expressed his urgency to change my approach. My scorecard had a short lifespan. Somehow, however, I managed to keep my job.

Where did I go wrong? Is scoring real safety performance a bad idea? My mistake was that I did not communicate the purpose and intent of the scorecard, and I embarrassed important people. The moral of the story is that you have to develop your scorecards as a team to gain the greatest value. Your team cannot fear the score. The goal is for your leaders to embrace measurement techniques and play to win. The prize is a better quality of life for your employees.

Ever since my initial scorecard experience, I have implemented similar systems with better results. Buy-in from the appropriate parties is the key to success. Stack-ranking performance in critical safety systems identifies your company's weaknesses, and it sparks a sense of responsibility in those who do not want to finish in the red.[1]

For Principle 1, you will learn five practices that demonstrate management commitment. The goal is to provide examples for how you can get your leadership team engaged in the safety processes that produce positive safety results. The focus is on corrective action follow-up, strategic visibility, PEAK Safety Dialogues, event analysis participation, and accountability. Your mission is to evaluate how well your company implements these practices. Look for areas where you can improve, and put a plan in place to make it happen. With the right focus on character, mentality, and results, you will make a difference.

---

1. *AIST Magazine* October 2010, Deliberate Accountability: Measure and Score Leading Indicators, David G. Lynn, CSP)

Practice #1 - Set the Standard with Management Safety Visibility. Do they know your name?

When I worked as a corporate health, safety, and environmental (HSE) director at Fluor, I supported large construction projects all over the world. Part of my responsibility was to help projects build strong safety cultures. On one occasion, I visited a job that was not meeting the company's safety expectations. I discovered part of the problem on the first morning that I was there. Each day, the workers would assemble in a large break tent before they dispersed to their work areas. The project leadership team would use this opportunity to communicate critical messages to the workforce.

I liked this standard method of communication, but I noticed a problem in the first five minutes of the meeting. The project manager stood up to talk to the group about safety, and he had to introduce himself to the crowd because no one knew who he was. He had never attended these meetings before, and he rarely walked the job. I did not expect everyone on the job site to know the project manager personally, but he had been employed there for more than a year. The workers should easily recognize their leader, and they should see the leader in a safety context on a regular basis. The fact that the workers did not know the project manager was one indicator of a lack of management engagement. The result was poor safety performance.

Safety commitment does not exist without visibility. Leaders can demonstrate their conviction to safety principles in strategic ways, and it does not have to cost the company money. A leader's presence in the right safety-related process will demonstrate what is important to the leader. Employees have to see visible actions that represent commitment.

One strategic visibility technique that leaders can use is to attend supervisor preshift meetings. Supervisors use preshift meetings to align teams before they start to work. Safety is a primary focus in these meetings. The preshift meeting should take the opportunity to identify critical steps, discuss potential safety hazards, and review injury prevention tools. This preplanning method is a cornerstone to safety success because leaders have to plan safety into every step. And the forum is a strategic opportunity for a manager to show a commitment to safety. A manager's presence demonstrates what is important to them.

Developing a Strategic Visibility Initiative: What Should It Look Like?

Step 1: Identify which managers and senior-level employees will participate in the process. Employees need to see decision-makers in a safety context on a consistent basis. Examples of leaders who should participate include plant managers, project managers, department managers, superintendents, general foremen, and any other leaders that a company will hold responsible for safety performance.

Step 2: Define how often you want designated leaders to partic- ipate. Daily participation is preferable, but is not always possible with the demands of a dynamic work environ- ment. Frequency is important, but consistency is also critical. Establish realistic expectations that you believe you can obtain.

Step 3: Develop a calendar and track participation. If you don't keep up with who fulfills their responsibilities, some workers will not participate at the levels you expect. Put names and dates on a board where everyone can see. Make the process visible, just like you do for other performance metrics. Why should safety be any different?

Step 4 : Hold leaders accountable for their participation. The goal is 100% compliance with the standards that a company establishes. Every leadership team has to decide how they will address employees who do not meet expectations. That accountability is why you have to have buy-in from all levels of the organization.

Step 5: Begin every leadership staff meeting with a strategic visibility moment. Have at least one person describe what they learned in their most recent preshift meeting. This discipline will help validate the process on a daily basis, and the discussion will hold leaders accountable for their activity in this critical process.

The five-step process is simple, but your team will have to commit their actions to the concept. As you roll out the strategic visibility initiative, prepare your team to address three common challenges:

Challenge No. 1 — Leaders will make comments like, "I don't have time to go to preshift meetings," or "I have other commitments that prevent my participation." While these comments may be legitimate, leaders must solve scheduling problems every day. This challenge is no different. Your team can find a collective solution. Organizations find the time to do the things that they feel add value to their business. A leadership presence in a safety context will definitely add value.

Challenge No. 2 — If workers are not used to seeing management in a preshift setting, they will wonder why you are there. Put their minds at ease and learn their names. Let workers know that you want to make a positive impact on safety. You want to demonstrate your commitment. Do not tell them, "Safety made me participate." That response does not help the process. Over time, your participation will become something each worker expects and appreciates.

Challenge No. 3 — A common question will arise when you introduce this strategic visibility practice. Leaders will ask, "What do you want me to do when I attend the preshift meeting?" The answer is simple. Ask safety-related questions. Workers know your interest by the questions you ask, and they gain respect for you as a leader when you help them. The following are some sample questions that a manager can ask during a preshift meeting:

What are the critical steps in your job?

What is the worst thing that could happen?

How do you prevent the worst thing from happening?

How can I help you prevent a potential injury?

Do you feel like you get the proper safety training?

Do you feel like you get the proper instructions to perform tasks safely?

Do you feel comfortable stopping work if a hazard is present?

How do people around you demonstrate their commitment to safety?

Do you have the appropriate tools to complete your work safely?

Do you believe that all incidents (injuries, near misses, first aids, etc.) can be prevented?

> Is there anything safety-related you would like for me to evaluate?
>
> If you could make one safety improvement, what would you do?

A safety culture does not exist without management visibility and engagement. An important step in building the culture is to make sure employees know your name. Establish organizational safe habits that promote engagement. That way, workers can sense your sincere dedication to their safety. Consistent attendance at preshift meetings provides a forum for leaders to engage their workforce with useful dialogue. The benefit is that leaders can identify opportunities for safety improvements while they get to know their workforce.[2]

Practice #2 - A PEAK Safety Dialogue - Prevention Begins with a Conversation

Have you ever asked the question, "What else can I do to improve our safety culture?" The answer may be in your next conversation. One of the most common safety weaknesses I see in organizations is a lack of management engagement with employees. As a general rule, leaders support safety wholeheartedly from behind a computer, but they fail to gain the value of personal interaction with employees in a safety context. The result is that workers develop a lack of trust and frustration in management's commitment to safety. At the same time, we ask, "What else can I do?" The remarkable solution is that we need to talk to people.

In 2016, I helped one of my clients identify ways they could improve their safety culture. The first step was to conduct a baseline safety performance assessment. I introduced them to our "Principle to Practice Safety Scorecard." The process utilizes a standard protocol that measures the effectiveness of critical

---

2. *Iron & Steel Technology,* AIST.org, Oct. 2018

safety principles and practices such as management commitment. We compared how my client demonstrated management safety commitment versus how industry leaders demonstrate safety commitment.

Management commitment is one of the most important elements that you can evaluate in your program. Without management commitment to safety, a company cannot achieve "best in class" results. For example, a typical corporate mission statement shows management commitment to safety on paper, but our scorecard measures how well the commitment is translated to the workforce. If the safety commitment is not visible and consistent, it does not exist in the minds of workers.

The assessment took one week to complete. The result revealed that the client had a safety management system, but they did not score well in the management commitment category. They did not have effective ways to engage employees. In other words, they did not talk with their workers about safety on a frequent basis. They did not participate in safety audits, safety meetings, or prejob briefs, and they did not make it a habit to approach people about safety. The management team had minimal visibility in a safety context. They supported safety from behind their computer, and they delegated all of the "safety responsibilities" to the safety professional. This lack of engagement created a huge gap between the workers and management. Their safety program existed only on paper.

To fill this gap between commitment on paper and commitment in reality, we introduced a **PEAK Safety Dialogue** process. The simple PEAK acronym is an error-prevention tool that raises situational awareness with a conversation.

The initiative required the plant manager, the staff, and the department managers to leave their meetings and walk into the plant and engage employees face-to-face. They committed to do this once a week using the PEAK Safety Dialogue format. The technique raises situational awareness with progressive questions about critical steps, potential errors, consequences, and controls. The PEAK Safety Dialogue provides a forum for all leaders to learn what workers deal with on a daily basis. While gaining a better understanding of the risk with each step, leaders also developed a relationship with workers in a safety context.

The PEAK Safety Dialogue responsibilities included:

- Once a week, the plant manager, staff, and department managers performed a PEAK Safety Dialogue.

- They observed a specific operation and they talked to a minimum of two people.

- They used the PEAK Safety Dialogue tool for their talking points.

- They asked employees about the following elements:
  - **P** – Plan critical steps of your job. (What are your critical steps?)
  - **E** – Evaluate risk and worst-case scenarios. (What is the worst thing that could happen?)
  - **A** - Anticipate how you are most likely to make an error. (What is a common mistake?)
  - **K** – Know your controls. (How do you protect yourself from injuries and errors?)

- They documented what they learned on the back of the card.

- They turned the cards in to the safety coordinator.

- The safety coordinator tracked participation and recorded good ideas.

The intent for the PEAK Safety Dialogue is to:

1. Establish a relationship with your workforce in a safety context.
2. Make yourself HIGHLY visible with safety.
3. Talk to people about step-by-step safety in their work environment.
4. Learn something about the process.
5. Find a way to make an improvement.
6. Show support and take ownership of safety.
7. Make a difference in safety performance by engaging the workforce in a useful manner.

The Intent for the PEAK Safety Dialogue is NOT to:

1. Develop a long "to-do" list for the safety coordinator.
2. Pass off the safety responsibilities to others.
3. "Get in the weeds" with every little detail.

The value of the program was a visible demonstration of consistent safety commitment. Leaders developed relationships with employees in the PEAK Safety Dialogue forum and improvements followed.

To promote the program, the leadership team adopted a strategic communication strategy. The first step was to train the participants on how to execute an effective PEAK Safety Dialogue. They also had to communicate the intent of the program to everyone in the plant. The communication process included four areas of focus.

1) Verbal Communications – Talk about the PEAK Safety Dialogue in a variety of settings. **2)** Visual Communications – Make the program visible everywhere you go in the plant. **3)** Written Communications – Keep the message alive through documentation. **4)** Informal Communications – Leverage the momentum of the program and create a "buzz" around PEAK Engagement.

The communication strategy included this list of actions:

1. Teach PEAK Safety Dialogue error-prevention classes.
2. Use the PEAK Safety Dialogue as a learning process in casual conversations.
3. Start every meeting with a Safety Topic that included a discussion about a PEAK Safety Dialogue.
4. Promote the PEAK Safety Dialogue in every safety training class.
5. Deliver a different PEAK Safety Dialogue safety topic each week.
6. Put up PEAK Safety Dialogue posters, banners, and table tents.
7. Document the procedure in the management system.
8. Participate in casual conversations that include PEAK Safety Dialogue elements.

The PEAK Safety Dialogue process was a huge success. The results of the original "Principle to Practice" scorecard magnified a common weakness that organizations experience with employee engagement. The PEAK Safety Dialogue was the solution. The process developed habits that encouraged leaders to approach people about safety. The systematic questions about steps, errors, consequences, and controls led to a better understanding of their processes. The insight improved situational awareness and built a stronger safety culture. The PEAK Safety Dialogue process is an example of how injury prevention can begin with a conversation.[3]

---

3. *EHS Today* Magazine, Jan. 15, 2019

Practice #3 - Get Involved with Event Analysis. The goal is to get leaders involved at the right levels.

The biggest challenge I have witnessed with event analysis processes (incident investigation) is that they are superficial in nature, and leaders in the organization do not participate in the analysis process. Organizations demonstrate these weaknesses when they assign the safety professional to fill out the form, and no one else gets involved. Without the benefit of multiple sources of input and leadership accountability, the process does not generate sustainable improvements. The organization does not show the workforce that they care about improvements.

The best programs have high expectations for executives, managers, and supervisors. That goal means management gets involved in each analysis step.

Step 1: Notification. The first step in getting all levels of the organization involved is to tell the appropriate people that an event occurred. When I worked at Fluor, our business group had an event reporting protocol. The protocol had specific requirements for who to contact and how quickly to make the call, based on the severity of the event. The protocol included elements such as:

- The severity dictated who the project leadership would inform. Example: If the event resulted in an OSHA recordable injury, the employee informed their supervisor. The supervisor informed their manager and the safety professional. The manager informed the project manager. The project manager told the executive responsible for the project. Within hours, everyone in the chain of command knew about the event, no matter where it happened in the world.

- There were timeframes for how fast an event was reported throughout the organization. If anyone in the chain of command failed to report the event appropriately, there were consequences. Fluor's expectation was that everyone responsible for the event needed to know as soon as possible. And you did not want an executive to know about the injury before your manager did! Communication had to happen fast.

- There were expectations for how soon the analysis should begin. For an OSHA recordable event, the analysis began after the first aid responder and safety team cared for the employee. By the end of the shift, the team had an initial report they could share with appropriate leaders. The initial report had basic information about the event, but it did not include a comprehensive root cause analysis. The detailed analysis had to be completed within 72 hours.

- There were expectations for the Project Manager to report to their executives what had happened and what they planned to do about the cause. This report had to be completed within 72 hours.

- Lost time cases required an executive in the business group to travel to the project and perform the investigation personally. The executive had to meet with the client and participate in all phases of the analysis, including identifying causes and corrective action plans.

Urgent focus on the notification process throughout the organization is a critical element of management commitment to safety.

Step 2: Build a Storyboard. The storyboard represents the sequence of events that led to the incident. To gain an accurate reflection of the timeline, you need the right people involved in collecting this information. At a minimum, this team would include the employee, the supervisor, the witnesses, and the safety professional. It is a mistake to leave this process in the hands of one person, such as a safety professional. The employee and the supervisor know more about the job than anyone else. Their detailed involvement in the process is essential. The supervisor should also help develop the storyboard because they are responsible for reporting the event to their chain of command. They have to own the results.

Step 3: Build Context. The storyboard is a critical first step that gives you a factual timeline for the event. It does not explain what the injured person thought at the time of the incident. The context of the event describes why it made sense to perform that task, and also the details associated with each critical step of the day. To establish the context, you need input from multiple layers of the organization. At a minimum, the following people should be involved: the employee, the supervisor, the safety professional, the witnesses, and the manager. Input from this group will help build context.

Step 4: Analyze the Facts. Once you know the details for the storyboard and the context, you can analyze the facts. At a minimum, the following people should be involved: the employee, the supervisor, the safety professional, the witnesses, the manager, and the senior site manager. When you get to this phase, each level of the organization should know the facts so that they can solve the problem.

Step 5: **Choose Points of Influence.** Where do you have the most influence? How can leaders in an organization assess an event and determine how they can influence safer decisions in the future? Based on the individual and organizational facts, look for points of influence that impact decisions and judgement. To accomplish this task, the following people should be involved; the employee, the supervisor, the safety professional, the witnesses, the manager, and the senior site manager.

Step 6: **Follow Up and Report Out.** The final step is to involve executives who are responsible for the site. If you have an effective reporting protocol, the executives should have an idea about the direction of the analysis, but you also need to have a formal system to report to the senior leaders.

When a Fluor project had a significant event (such as an OSHA recordable), the project manager had to arrange a conference call with the executive responsible for the site. The project manager had to walk the executive through a standard presentation deck that defined what happened, why it happened, and how they would prevent a repeat event. The project manager could not delegate the process to the safety professional. The project manager was responsible for all elements of the project to include OSHA recordable events. The executive conference call encouraged accountability throughout the organization.

The benefit of an intuitive root cause analysis process is that it improves organizational tools and techniques that prevent the errors in judgement that lead to injuries. BUT, you cannot make sustainable improvements without the involvement of employees, supervisors, managers, and executives. They are responsible for the site's performance!

Practice #4 - Where is the Accountability? Know the line... don't cross it.

How do you think that safety professionals across the world would answer this question: "What is the most frustrating issue you deal with as a safety professional?" I bet "a lack of accountability" would be at the top of the list. Noncompliance with rules, procedures, and programs is an indication of a poor safety culture. Great companies draw a line in the sand and they have established consequences for not following the rules.

Think about how rule enforcement works. Highway 123 connects my residence in Seneca, South Carolina, with my training center in Greenville, South Carolina. It is a short 35-mile trip that passes through two towns: Clemson, and Easley. I can think of three specific places where the police sit with their radar guns. They are not there every day, but you can see where the grass is worn on the side of the road where the police park. I know without a doubt that if I travel that path on a consistent basis, they will record my speed. They do not forgive noncompliance, and the consequences are clear. You get a ticket if you speed through these areas.

The question is, "How does that consistent enforcement influence my behavior?" I DRIVE THE SPEED LIMIT! It is a simple concept. When you have clear expectations and consistent enforcement, people follow the rules.

How do you apply the same concept in a work environment? You can look at accountability in two different areas:

1) Accountability for basic rules.

2) Accountability for fulfilling your responsibilities for your job position.

Critical Steps to Build Accountability with Basic Rules:

1. Develop clear rules and regulations for people to follow.
2. Make the rules simple to understand.
3. Define the consequences for noncompliance.
4. Train and communicate the expectations relentlessly.
5. Apply consistent and just disciplinary action for noncompliance.

When I worked at OSHA as a Compliance Officer, I visited over 200 different sites in a three-year period. Every company produced something different, but the rules were similar. I experienced a similar perspective when I worked with Fluor. We performed contract/construction work for clients all over the world. Every safety orientation that I sat through had the same OSHA rules to follow. The difference between the good and the great safety cultures was the ability to hold people accountable to the rules. You knew where the "speed traps" were, and you did not break the rules because they were clear, simple, evident, and consistently enforced.

There are some obstacles to overcome. I have also been in some environments where the rules were enforced ONLY if the safety professional saw the noncompliance. This type of "safety police" culture will not build a "best in class" safety culture. Supervisors and managers have to take the initiative to enforce the rules based on the clear guidelines and consequences. Safety cultures have the potential to succeed when leaders take ownership of employee accountability.

Accountability for Fulfilling Your Responsibilities for Your Job Position

Accountability is essential to prevent injuries, but what does it mean to hold someone accountable for safety and keep score on their performance? This is often a deficient part of safety programs because leaders wait until something bad happens before they feel the need to hold anyone accountable. It is too late after a negative event to hold someone accountable for safety. The answer to accountability is simple: set standards for the people, and track the results.

For example, if audits are required, track audit participation and measure the quality of audits. If an organization values sustained corrective action, track the number of repeat observations on each audit. If a program requires supervisors to perform preshift safety meetings, track the quality and participation in the process. The records become a performance measurement. Tracking prompts rewards for achievement and consequences for failure to meet standards. True accountability means that if you do not meet your standard, you use progressive motivation to drive your desired results. The consequences can include termination. Remember, this is life or death. You cannot have a soft reaction for leaders who do not meet safety standards. This is a perfect opportunity to instill expectations, urgency, and discipline into your program.

You can look at accountability from two perspectives: rule enforcement and responsibilities for safety processes. If expectations are clear, just, evident, and enforced in both categories, the safety culture will evolve in a positive direction. But, if you only post the speed limit sign and you never write any tickets, people will follow their own rules. Accountability is that simple.

Practice #5 - Don't Forget Corrective Action.

Why are corrective action measures so hard to sustain? I believe it is because we do not focus on why the problem exists in the first place. We simply modify the surface, and forget the reason it made sense for the condition or behavior to exist in the first place. And then we wonder why the problem still exists two weeks later. Sometimes we fail to sustain corrective actions because we do not know how to correct the problem. Instead, we do just enough to satisfy the right people. And there will be the inevitable issues with time, money, and commitment. All of these problems are real, but you cannot let them deter you from your mission. You have to push forward.

Here are a few of the biggest corrective action frustrations that I have faced in my career.

Number One: I have conducted hundreds of audits that have produced noncompliance or unsafe observations. Many of the responsible people would correct the items in front of me. So the supervisor checks the "corrected" box and moves on to the next task for the day. But if you walk by the same issue tomorrow, what do you think you will find? More than likely, you can spot the same noncompliance or unsafe condition. The question is, "Was the issue really corrected?" And the answer is no.

Number Two: Root Cause Analysis programs generate corrective actions. The corrective actions go on someone's "to do" list. That person knows that someone is going to follow up on the action until they are satisfied that the problem is "corrected." So they do just enough to satisfy whoever is watching. In some cases, no one is really watching. That makes it easy. After enough time has passed, you just delete the item because it does not seem relative any longer.

Number Three: You find yourself in a discussion about something safety related. The general consensus is that someone needs to do something about the "issue." No one takes ownership, and the conversation ends. A couple of weeks later, a group of people find themselves deep in discussion about the same thing. But again, no one takes ownership of the issue. The problem continues.

I am a sure as safety professionals you understand what I am talking about when it comes to sustainable corrective action. You can add your personal frustrations to the list. The bottom line is that sometimes issues are corrected on the surface, but they do not stay corrected. Other times, safety issues are merely the topic of conversation with no ownership or resolution.

The goal is to set your program up in a way that minimizes these frustrations. Here are ten tips for successful sustainable corrective action:

1. **Correct the immediate hazard.** Sometimes you have to implement temporary measures to make the situation safe. You cannot afford to let open and obvious safety issues exist without some level of attention.

2. **Understand why the safety issue exists.** If you do not address the "why" the behavior or condition came to exist, you will not correct the problem in the long term.

3. **DO NOT rely on "training" alone as your corrective action.** If training is a component of your corrective action, something went wrong with the original training. Identify what went wrong with the original training, and then correct the problem.

4. **ALWAYS include some type of long-term communication strategy for the changes.** If you do not plan how you will communicate the improvement long-term, I can assure you that people will forget what happened. They will drift back to their normal state.

5. **ALWAYS include some level of auditing in the corrective action.** The audit is especially important for behavior-related issues. People do not change an unsafe habit simply because you told them to "stop doing that" once. You have to implement a consistent strategy in order to monitor and observe progress.

6. **Maintain a corrective action log for all open items.** The log should include audit observations, root cause analysis corrective actions, and general suggestions from employees. Be sure to track the issues.

7. **Assign who is responsible for making the improvement.** No one will correct anything until their name is on the list. Accountability is your only hope for improvement.

8. **Set target dates and track the audit item to completion.** People need a deadline and motivation to complete a task.

9. **Senior-level managers should meet weekly to review the corrective action log.** If you do not establish a meeting time, the action items lose their urgency.

10. **HOLD PEOPLE ACCOUNTABLE!** This requirement is the most important part of the program. Track who is doing their job and who needs some motivation. Track repeat items. Transparency about safety issues that resurface on a regular basis will show you weak links in your leadership organization.

The frustration is real. To minimize the obstacles, establish a structured strategy that applies these tips. Over time, you will see that the methodical approach makes a difference. You can accumulate a history of success stories, and take pride in the culture you have built.

Principle 1 Summary – Management Commitment and Engagement

Visible management commitment is the cornerstone to success, and it is a mark that distinguishes a culture. I wish everyone who was committed to safety had a green ear. Would that not make life easier? If you faced a complicated safety issue, you would know who could give you sound safety direction. You would know exactly who to count on for keeping people safe in your work environment. A distinguishing mark could indicate everyone's safety expectations. On the flip side of the coin, you would also know exactly how to identify people who are not engaged in safety. People with a green ear represent commitment, and they could influence those without a green ear.

Unfortunately, physical features cannot outwardly reveal safety commitment, but visible consistent behaviors do measure a commitment to safety. Our words and actions project our commitment, and we have to ask ourselves difficult questions requiring honest reflection on our approach to safety. These reflections are important to discover a true commitment to safety. All of our actions represent a footprint for safety, and we project an image whether we like it or not. How would your coworkers describe your focus on safety? Do you have a green ear for safety? You may not come to work with a green ear, but you have opportunities every day to demonstrate that you believe an injury-free culture is possible.

PRINCIPLE 2
Employee Involvement

What separates the good from the great in safety? How do you connect all of the dots so that your organization works injury free? Leaders across multiple industries struggle with this question because they have a desire to send people home in one piece, yet employees continue to get hurt. To achieve top ten results, you have to consider what drives a high-performance safety program. Companies that excel in safety share at least one common characteristic. Employees are highly engaged in the safety process, and they play to win!

Think about sports. Who is more invested in the game? The spectator watching a game on TV? The fan with a seat in the stands? Or the players on the field? All these people somehow support the game, and they all want to win, but someone has to do the work. Players are one hundred percent invested in the outcome of the game. That mindset is also true when you build a safety culture. You will have spectators that watch from a computer screen. There are also managers that cheer for the results, but the most invested people are the employees who put in the work and play to win with safety.

You can create an atmosphere where your workforce is one

hundred percent invested in the safety culture. And the employees are the ones who benefit! To achieve this company-wide mindset, make sure you value people, build trust, show respect, and let the employees own the results.

Value People

People want to work for employers who see and treat them as individuals, and not as statistics. While safety metrics are always important, in order to build an injury-free culture you must ask, "How do I visibly put people first? Am I building mutual respect?" When the focus shifts from a number to a person, safety initiatives gain value—and a sense of urgency. This change encourages people to take ownership of safety. Sincere ownership and involvement will enable safety success.

Build Trust and Respect

People respond better to leaders they trust and respect. Trust and respect come from the relationships you build in your work environment. You have to earn these qualities – but rest assured, they have a powerful impact in your work environment.

Own the Result

You have spectators and you have players. Avid fans watch the game, but players have the ultimate fulfillment. They make the sacrifices necessary to win. Strong safety cultures get employees involved, and then the employees want to make the sacrifices necessary to win. Just like players benefit from the outcome of a game, employees benefit from their efforts to achieve top ten results. Imagine a work environment where management enables each employee to participate in the game. The potential is unlimited.

The goal for Principle 2 is to offer five suggestions for how you can transition spectators into players in your work environment.

With hazard identification processes, safety champion programs, mentoring processes, "approaching others" campaigns, and audit participation, you can offer meaningful ways for people to get involved. Cultivate a spirit of engagement with a cause to rally around, and you will build a safety culture that drives success.

Practice #1 - Find It – Fix It! If you don't look you will not find it.

One winter, I visited a drilling project in a remote part of Alberta, Canada. The employees incorporated the concept of hazard identification into their daily routine for good reason. The weather was extreme, the conditions were harsh, and the job had risks. The work was remote, and there were countless challenges to overcome. On a typical winter morning, the temperature was below zero. Small crews would assemble in the wilderness to operate drill rigs. As you can imagine, the work required an enormous amount of attention to ensure no one got hurt.

The crew would start each morning with a prejob brief to review critical steps, hazards, and controls. While prejob briefs are not uncommon, this company implemented a twist that I thought was unique. After the brief, everyone was required to go to their work area, find a hazard, and fix the hazard before they could start work. Each employee recorded what they corrected every morning. I liked the process: **1)** The job had extreme conditions and considerable risk. **2)** Injury prevention required a consistent and disciplined approach for hazard identification. **3)** The foreman required EVERYONE to participate. **4)** Multiple perspectives generated numerous results that improved safety. **5)** The crews learned to scrutinize safety in a positive way. **6)** The deliberate action elevated situational awareness. **7)** They found hazards and they corrected hazards. **8)** The discipline was a daily learning opportunity.

This company developed a positive way to involve employees in hazard identification. The approach was successful for this company, but the key is for you to find the best application for your business. How can you implement the same concept in a way that has an equal impact?

Follow these seven steps to incorporate a similar program at your company.

Step 1: **Require all employees to participate in hazard identification.** The program has multiple benefits, but the number one goal is to get people involved. Employees need to own safety in their area. The value of the program extends beyond just what people find and fix. The process creates the habit to look for risk. That habit becomes a natural way that the person does business. They develop ownership of their safety. That sense of ownership is a process that EVERYONE should have.

Step 2: **Define how often you want people to participate.** Choose a reasonable goal that you can manage. If you say that you want people to turn in one "find it – fix it" observation a week, you have to have the capability to track the process. Set goals that you can achieve. Make the expectation fit your organization.

Step 3: **Outline the process to submit the hazards they find and fix.** Create a simple form that people can use to submit ideas. Include suggestions for hazard identification, and provide clear instructions for how they submit the observations.

Step 4: **Train and communicate the expectations of the program.** When you implement the program, some employees will roll their eyes and complain about one more thing that they have to do. The training and communication process will establish the expectations. Explain why hazard identification is important, and why you want them involved. The pitch is an easier sell when people know they can get something out of the process. Motivate people with rewards and recognition. People will also ask, "What do you want me to look for?" Prepare a top 10 list of relevant safety issues. The list will jump start the identification process.

Step 5: Track progress and participation with the program. Tracking the results is the biggest challenge in the process. How do you keep up with the participation? Think through the details so that you do not overextend your capabilities. If you have a lot of people participating, track the total number of cards submitted. You do not have to focus on participation from every single person. Track a percentage of participation. For example, if you have 100 people in the program and you get 75 cards, you have a 75% participation rate. Review responses to make sure people record legitimate issues.

Step 6: Review responses and provide feedback. A natural tendency is for people to submit observations or comments that may or may not represent a real hazard. Make an effort to evaluate the cards and follow up on legitimate safety issues. Talk to the people who submit great finds. The process will gain momentum when people know their comments make a difference.

Step 7: Recognize and reward people who excel. To generate interest and enthusiasm, reward people! Recognize exceptional participation. Programs die fast when there is no energy behind the process. Find small ways to motivate people, and make recognition a critical component of your overall process.

The secret formula to great hazard identification is to find ways to engage employees in the process. 1) Establish a consistent and disciplined approach. 2) Expect EVERYONE to participate. 3) Treat the process as a learning tool. 4) Emphasize how important it is to elevate situational awareness on a daily basis. 5) Make the process valuable. Make it fun! The benefit is obvious. More involvement identifies more hazards. Fewer hazards will minimize the opportunity for injuries.

Practice #2 - Develop Safety Champions

A safety champion identifies risk and addresses issues. Find champions of your program, and use their leadership abilities to monitor safety. Build relationships with the natural leaders at work, and earn their trust and respect. Give your Safety Teams and Committees a problem to solve. I am not a fan of Safety Committees that meet and complain about their problems. I want to lead teams that make positive change.

The following example describes how you can address a specific trend with employee involvement.

Making a Hands-On Connection

By David Lynn

Every scar on your hand has a story. The key to improving workplace hand safety is helping others see and feel the same lesson that you learned from your hand injury – without the pain.

When I spoke at an *EHS Today*/Dyneema forum during the 2014 ASSE Professional Development Conference and Expo in Orlando, Florida, I conducted an informal hand safety poll. I asked the audience: "How many people have cut their hands?" Everyone in the room raised their hand.

When I asked how many people have had stitches on one of their hands, many people in the room kept their hands raised. Then I asked, "How many people have had stitches more than once?" In a room full of safety professionals, I learned that most people have scraped their hands, and many have had stitches multiple times.

Every scar on your hand has a story to tell and a lesson that you learned the hard way. The key to improving workplace hand safety is helping others see and feel the same lesson that you learned from your hand injury – without the pain.

Several years ago, I used a utility knife to cut plastic. The plastic was harder than I expected, and I had to apply pressure to make the cut. When I applied the pressure, the blade broke and my hand slammed into the broken blade that was stuck in the plastic. I didn't want to look at the damage, because I knew that I had made a mistake. The incident caused me to acquire six stitches and a good dose of humility.

As a result of the incident, I cringe every time I see a utility knife. I have a personal, hands-on connection with the risk. A productive hand safety initiative helps others see the reality of the risk without the painful experience.[4]

Zero Excuses for Workplace Hand Injuries

The **Hands-On Safety Champion Program** is a process that reduces hand injuries using employee involvement and a hands-on reality check. I cringe when I see a utility knife, and my instinct is to pull back when I have to use one because I remember my lesson. The goal of the program is to instill the same instinctive reaction in others, but without the pain.

---

4. First published in *EHS Today,* by David G. Lynn, CSP, Oct. 13, 2014. Source: http://ehstoday.com/hand-protection/making-hands-connection

Here's how the Hands-On Safety Champion Program works.

You choose natural leaders (champions) in your workforce and give them the responsibility to focus on hand safety. The program is a 360-degree process that promotes identification, coaching, and mentoring through positive peer-to-peer influence.

The champion and the person he or she mentors ask people about hand safety, and then initiate conversations about hand protection. For example, they can compare scars! That conversation starter might sound strange, but I guarantee if you tell the story of one of your scars, coworkers will follow up with their own version. That exchange is a "hands-on" connection, and the common ground makes it easier to discuss how to protect your hands. The goal is to help people think about safety-related questions. Each person you talk to is a coaching contact.

Champions conduct focused hand-safety surveys with survey cards. The cards have ten specific bullet points that help champions evaluate the common risks that cause hand injuries. Champions also use the platform to coach and mentor coworkers. The focused surveys are an opportunity to share their stories to make a hands-on connection.

On the back of the card, there are safety-topic talking points related to the survey items. Champions can use the talking points during safety meetings and prejob briefings. Champions should try to review these items with as many people as possible to raise awareness about hand safety. These conversations are yet another opportunity to make a hands-on connection.

After the champion completes the survey, he or she shows the results to a supervisor and then forwards it to the program administrator. At a minimum of once a month, champions should review the findings as a group and discuss how to improve negative trends. The group should include the supervisors and the program administrator.

Step 1: **Select your Safety Champions.** You need good people to lead the charge. Each supervisor should appoint a safety champion for his or her team. The champions lead the initiative to coach, mentor, and observe safe hand behavior in their areas. Safety champions should possess the following qualities:

- Positive attitude
- Strong leadership skill
- Interest in safety.
- Attention to detail (or conscientiousness)
- A desire to achieve safety goals

Step 2: **Clarify Responsibility.** Once you have selected your hands-on safety champions, communicate their responsibilities to the group.

For example, safety champions are responsible for:
1. Performing weekly hands-on surveys.
2. Coaching and mentoring other employees.
3. Approaching and coaching others who engage in unsafe behavior.

Supervisors are responsible for:
1. Making sure safety champions are able to perform hands-on surveys.
2. Supporting the safety champions.
3. Meeting weekly with the safety champions.

Program administrators are responsible for:
1. Leading the Hands-On Safety Champion Program.
2. Coaching and mentoring the safety champions.
3. Meeting frequently with the safety champions.

Step 3: **Deploy the Process.** Champions conduct surveys focused on specific areas of hand safety. They also help coach and mentor employees, and they use these opportunities to share their stories. The safety champions choose one or more people to accompany them on observation walks, during which they use a survey card with hand-safety audit items. These walks are a perfect opportunity to make a hands-on connection with coworkers by sharing personal examples of the consequences of poor hand safety. Telling your story makes it real.

Conclusion

The **Hands-On Safety Champion Program** facilitates a discussion about common ground hand safety. The platform enables you to share the stories behind your scars, and instill caution in coworkers. I know what it is like to cut my hand using a utility knife. If I conduct a focused hand safety survey, do you think I can provide insight to someone using a similar tool? Empower your hands-on safety champions to share the same message.

The Hands-On Safety Champion Program works. The key is to select the right people and give them specific tasks that they can control. Be sure to provide consistent communication and support to your team. Make it a privilege to serve on the Hands-On Safety Champion Team, and emphasize the importance of each team member's role to encourage others in the workforce.

The scars on our hands are common ground for us, and each scar has a story. When you tell that story, you make a hands-on connection that can inspire your team members to work safer and go the extra mile to protect their hands.

Practice #3: Create Mentors - We learn to do our jobs from the people who do not have official titles.

New employees do not want to get hurt, and they often have questions about their jobs. The goal of an employee new hire mentoring program is to teach new employees to do their jobs safely. You cannot learn how to do all the parts of your job in the classroom. As a new employee, you accumulate useful knowledge from listening to an instructor, but you learn the practical hands-on functions of your job from those you work with every day. On-the-job training is a natural part of everyone's learning process. An employee peer-to-peer mentoring program utilizes trusted employees to develop positive safety attitudes and disseminate critical information to new employees. This concept is similar to a Safety Champion Program, but the difference is the mentor's focus. The mentor focuses on training new employees in their first 30 days, while the Safety Champion Program focuses on monitoring behaviors and conditions throughout the life of the job.

I understand the power of hands-on training. When I started work as a Compliance Officer at OSHA in 1992, I spent the majority of my first four months in a room the size of two cubicles, along with four other people. The objective was to learn the OSHA standards. We studied like this every day for four months! Can you imagine spending eight hours a day, five days a week trapped in a small room staring at the Code of Federal Regulations? How exciting is that? Better yet, how effective is that?

The training was not an orientation, but rather an initiation. I do not know how much I learned during the first four months in my OSHA role, but I – along with my coworkers – survived the imprisonment. The next stage of the program was much more useful. We shadowed experienced Compliance Officers on their inspections, and I began to see how people did the job I would learn to do. The experienced Compliance Officers were my mentors, and they taught me the hands-on details of the job. In the field is where I really learned the most. Over the next nine months, I learned every facet of the inspection and report-writing process from a mentor. As I progressed, the Compliance Officers would let me do more of the job. It was an incremental process that taught me the details. After a year, I passed a final evaluation and began performing inspections solo.

The lesson I learned in my OSHA experience is that "book learning" is important—but it is not where you learn how to do your job. You learn your job from people. Companies with a history of exceptional safety performance have systems that take advantage of the power of peer-to-peer learning. If you give safety-minded employees an opportunity to instill their safety values into new employees via mentoring, you will perpetuate a culture that embraces safety.

An effective mentoring program should accomplish specific goals.

Step 1: Identify safety-conscious leaders in your workforce. Every company has natural leaders in their work environment. They may not have a leadership title, but you know that people go to them with questions. Employees trust them. Utilize this natural social norm to develop your mentoring program.

Step 2: Train the mentors. Empower your mentors to utilize their influence for the safety good. Explain how the process works, and let your participants know how important their role is. Explain your expectations for how they will evaluate and coach employees. Mentors have an opportunity to influence the next generation of workers in their company. The training should give the mentors a sense of pride in their contributions.

Step 3: Identify the new employees and let them know who their mentor is. Companies can do this in multiple ways. You can provide new employee stickers for hardhats. You can have new employees wear new employee vests. You can do whatever fits the culture of your company. The benefit is that mentors know who they need to help.

Step 4: Establish a way to evaluate and coach new employees. The purpose of the step is to confirm that new employees know and understand critical safety information. The evaluation is a coaching tool, and not a performance measurement tool.

The goal for the mentoring program is to add structure to the way employees learn to do their jobs. The process empowers natural leaders to train new people. The classroom environment is an introduction to safety. The reality is that our coworkers teach us how to do our jobs safely. If you can harness this social dynamic in a positive way, you will have a powerful safety impact on the next generation of workers.

Practice #4: Approaching Others - Say something!

I learned the power of "Approaching Others" when I was the EHS Engineer at Duracell. We made AA and AAA batteries at our plant. One day I was walking through the Cell Assembly department in a rush to attend a meeting, and I saw a battery on the floor in the middle of the aisle. I did not want to leave the slip hazard in the middle of the floor, so I instinctually kicked it under a machine. My reaction was similar to what many people do when they drop a piece of ice in front of their refrigerator. They kick it under the refrigerator… right?

Every operator in the area saw me kick the battery. You would have thought I committed a major crime. They made a point to approach me and remind me to pick up the batteries. Do not ever kick them under the equipment. For months, operators would not let me forget my transgression. Most of the reminders were good natured harassment, but their willingness to approach me made a huge impression. I never kicked another battery. I knew people were watching my every move, and they would approach me if I stepped out of bounds. It is a lot like the ice on the floor of the kitchen. If my wife is watching, I pick up the ice!

Teaching people to approach others is one of the most important ways that you can engage employees in a safe environment. They need to feel their responsibility to help each other. Ask yourself an honest question. Is your workforce eager to approach people who do things in an unsafe manner? My experience is that most people would like to think they would stop someone from doing something unsafe, but in reality, most people hesitate. You have to promote and cultivate a positive Approaching Others culture.

The first step is to recognize why people hesitate to approach someone. Here are five reasons:

1. **Lack of general awareness** – In theory, people will acknowledge that a task has a certain level of risk. But often they do not believe they will get hurt. This overconfidence leads to a lack of general awareness or sensitivity to the risk.

2. **Fear of rejection** – When people do not receive our message in a positive way, we feel rejected. Their negative response can have a significant impact on our willingness to approach the next person.

3. **Lack of confidence** – Everyone does not have an extroverted personality. Approaching people about something they are doing unsafely is not a natural behavior for some people. Repetition and support are important to build confidence.

4. **Fear of judgement** – Some people recognize some hazards because they have performed the same task. They understand

the risk first-hand. If they say something, the person may wonder, "Who are you to tell me not to do that? You have done the same thing!"

5. **Uncertainty** - We hesitate when we are not sure about what we see. Not everyone has the same level of safety knowledge. You may observe something that looks unsafe, but you are not positive. The lack of confidence causes the hesitation.

The second step to build a positive Approaching Others culture is to help people overcome the obstacles.

One of the hardest things for most people to do is to start a conversation. Extroverts think this is a crazy statement, but I know it is fact. I am an introvert. When I worked with OSHA as a Compliance Officer, my heart would beat out of my chest before every inspection because the idea of approaching a stranger with a safety concern petrified me. The idea of approaching someone I did not know is an unnatural action, but my responsibility as a safety professional has helped me overcome many of the obstacles mentioned above. Here are a few ways that you can make the process come naturally.

1. **Give people a goal.** Challenge your workforce to intentionally approach one person a day about something safety related.

2. **Create an expectation** that Approaching Others is a responsibility, and not just a suggestion. Ask people this question every day. Did you approach anyone today? Follow up will support the expectation.

3. **Give people confidence** by providing specific issues that they can look for every day. Training, communication, and consistent monitoring will help build confidence.

4. **Eliminate judgement** by communicating various safety topics about Approaching Others. Communicate the importance of receiving and delivering feedback in a positive way.

5. **Promote the concept!** Your workforce should see and hear about Approaching Others from everyone. Make it visible with posters, banners, and postings.

The third step is to develop an implementation strategy. Here are few ideas.

1. **Put together an Approaching Others Steering Team.** You need leaders from across your organization to champion the process.

2. **Develop a Top 10 Approach List.** If you want people to build confidence in what they correct, you have to point them in the right direction. The list gives them a starting point.

3. **Conduct Approaching Others training for all employees.** Train people on how important it is to help each other out. Help people think about how they will feel if someone gets hurt when they could have prevented it. Instill a sense of ownership.

4. **Deliver weekly Approaching Others safety topics.** People need to hear a consistent message over time to build a habit. Weekly safety topics can help instill the message. Cover subjects like:

   ○ How to give and receive feedback
   ○ How to approach a leader
   ○ How to handle difficult situations
   ○ How to help a new employee
   ○ How to take responsibility
   ○ How to take advantage of "fresh eyes"
   ○ How to handle resistance

5. **Promote with posters, banners, and table tents.** People need to see the message everywhere. Create a marketing campaign that makes the topic a part of the way people think.

6. **Have Approaching Others safety topics before meetings.** If you have three or more people in a meeting, choose one person to describe their last Approaching Others moment.

This request will help make people accountable. The expectation will also raise situational awareness in multiple settings every day.

7. **Develop Approaching Others contact cards.** Find a way to record who is approached and who is actually Approaching Others. If you track a process, you have a better opportunity for success.

8. **Find a way to incentivize Approaching Others.** Reward the most active participants. Build a buzz around the mindset. This focus will help make it a habit.

The process is a mindset that embraces the personal responsibility to help. There is a tremendous benefit to cultivating a positive culture that encourages Approaching Others when something is unsafe. Employees reinforce safety principles that you promote. They look for hazards and take ownership of correcting them. The positive atmosphere builds a culture that prevents injuries.

Practice #5: Help with Audits - Employees see the issue first.

You know your job better than anyone. Several years ago, one of my safety professional friends had an OSHA inspection on their construction project. As usual, the project team was anxious to see what the OSHA Inspector found. As they walked through the job, my friend would cringe if he saw something out of compliance, and then he would wonder if the OSHA Inspector saw the same thing. To my friend's surprise, the OSHA Inspector did not recognize everything my friend saw during the site walk.

The site safety team was surprised. Why did the OSHA Inspector miss so many noncompliance observations when they were obvious to the site safety team? There are a couple of explanations. 1) The OSHA Inspector may not have been very good at his job. 2) The OSHA inspector just did not see the job with the same level of detail and experience as someone who is there every day.

The reason for missing the observations could be a blend of both scenarios. The event teaches a great lesson. Nobody knows your job like you do! You see the details better than any visitor or OSHA Inspector because you are sensitive to the surroundings. You know where to look. Apply this reality to your workforce. As much as you think you know about your plant or project, the employees who do the work know more. Utilize this truth to help you find and correct hazards. Learn from the people who do the work, and help them see your perspective.

The Process:

Step 1: **Develop and implement a weekly audit process.** The goal is to identify and correct hazards in the workplace.

Step 2: **Define who is going to do the audits,** including when and where.

Step 3: **Include all levels of the organization in the audit schedule.** This group gives you an opportunity to get different perspectives. Take advantage of the knowledge of the people who do the jobs. Ask for their help to identify the hazards.

Step 4: **Track audit observations and corrective action measures.**

Step 5: **Rotate different employees into the audits.** Expose as many people as possible to the practice of looking for opportunities to make your company safer.

As much as you think you know about your plant or project, the employees who do the work know more. Employees also are the ones who are most invested in the risk. They want to make their jobs safer, and if you include them in the audit process, they have an opportunity to help. Everyone involved can learn from each other.

Principle 2 Summary – Employee Involvement

Everyone has to participate and take ownership of safety in a mature injury-free culture. That inclusiveness is why employee involvement is such a critical part of OSHA's Voluntary Protection Program. I have witnessed OSHA representatives interview fifty percent of a workforce to gauge the level of employee participation. They are serious about employee involvement, because they know what a huge impact it has on safety performance.

If you can establish a safety framework that values employees, builds trust, and shows respect for each employee, the results will take care of themselves. The goal for Principle 2 is to offer five suggestions for how you can transition spectators into players in your work environment. With hazard identification processes, safety champion programs, mentoring processes, approaching others campaigns, and audit participation, you can offer meaningful ways for people to get involved. Cultivate a spirit of engagement with a cause to rally around, and you will build a safety culture that drives success.

PRINCIPLE 3
Safety Training and Communication

Learning Culture

What is the first image that pops into your mind when I say, "Safety Training"? There is a reasonable chance that you think about a classroom setting with PowerPoint slides and an instructor. Classroom instruction is a common component of training, but is that the full picture? Is that where all valuable "learning" takes place?

I want to expand your idea of safety training, and help you develop systems that teach people about safety using multiple methods. The goal is to develop a learning culture because learning is leading! A learning culture impacts behavior and performance because it establishes a set of shared attitudes, values, goals, and practices that characterize a company or corporation.

Learning Climate

Create a climate where people want to learn about safety and health. You can establish formal and informal methods to create this environment. An effective safety training plan that promotes a learning culture has three layers: classroom training, coaching in the field, and general awareness communication. To achieve success at all three levels, organizations have to equip managers with knowledge. Value-added education goes beyond teaching an individual's specific skills. Meaningful training teaches people to think about what could happen. Leaders have to dedicate time to development, and they should have support systems in place to follow-up with positive (and negative) reinforcement. A strategic training plan will help develop a culture that includes proactive safety messages.

You will learn five practices that demonstrate how to develop a learning culture. The goal is to provide examples for how you can structure different levels of safety training. The focus is on safety orientations, basic regulatory schedules, safety leadership training, safety toolbox topics, and communication strategies. Your mission is to evaluate how well your company implements these practices. Look for areas where you can improve, and put a plan in place to make it happen. With the right character, mentality, and results focus, you will make a difference!

Practice #1: Safety Orientations - Make a good first impression.

How long does it take to make a first impression? I read the book *Blink* by Malcolm Gladwell. He described a study conducted by Psychologist Nalini Ambady. The study revealed that most people form their impressions of something within seconds. One study asked participants to rate professors on how effective they were. They showed participants videos of professors in lengths of 10, 5, and 2 seconds. The crazy thing is that the results were similar despite the length of the video. The moral of the story is that first impressions matter.

Apply the same first impressions thought process to daily

experiences. How long does it take you to determine that you do not want to eat at a restaurant? How long does it take you to formulate an impression of someone you interview? How long does it take you to feel comfortable in a group of strangers? How long does it take you to feel like a company is committed to safety? We form impressions within seconds.

Based on the idea that first impressions matter, what is one of the best ways to make a great safety impression on a new employee? Deliver an exceptional safety orientation. You can create a memorable experience that sets the tone for the employee's employment. When that employee steps on your site, you want them to know without a doubt that safety is important.

Consider the difference between good and bad safety impressions. What sets the stage for a bad impression?

Here are the **Top Four Obstacles** to forming a good first impression of safety:

1. **Last minute orientations** – I have experienced these numerous times in my career. I would start my day with a plan that did not include a safety orientation. Then, at the last minute, someone says, "Hey David, I need you to give this person a new hire orientation today. It is an emergency. We need them!" My day was immediately disrupted. Last minute training always frustrated me.

2. **Rushed to finish** – Emergencies mean I need them now! I have had department managers, construction managers, supervisors, and other leaders banging on the door to the orientation room asking, "When are you going to finish?" Urgency can have a negative impact on quality.

3. **Inadequate content and delivery** – As a contractor, I have sat through more than one orientation where the host representative shows you a video and says, "Sign here." That brief interaction was the extent of the orientation. I have also experienced orientations where a security guard, an administrative

assistant, or a human resource representative asks you to read a list of rules and sign a paper to confirm that you know the rules. The orientation is complete!

4. **Too far down the agenda** – Do not treat a safety orientation as an afterthought. If safety is not FIRST on the new hire agenda, you have missed the opportunity to make an exceptional first impression. On the new hire's first day, escort them straight to the training room for safety orientation. Establish the fact that safety really is "first" at your company.

These obstacles give new employees a bad first impression. A last minute, rushed, or abbreviated approach shows a new employee that safety is a "check the box" formality. A company will struggle to overcome that initial perception.

What sets the stage for a good impression?

1. **Dedicate classroom time on the first day.** If safety is a value and a top priority, start the work experience at your company with safety training. Secure a room that can accommodate the group, and kick off the day with required safety training. You want that person to think, "I did not know that I have to be a safety expert." The new hire will feel the importance of safety if you convey the urgency.

2. **Review safety content that covers basic OSHA requirements and company specific rules.** The OSHA rules are a tool to set priorities and expectations with safety. Talk about them in a manner that reflects the practical need in your specific work environment. Show people how this rule helps people at your company work safely. Explain the personal consequences of noncompliance (injury) and tell people how the company holds them accountable (disciplinary action). When the new hire leaves the class, you want them to think, "Wow! They mean business!"

3. **Utilize your workforce to talk about safety.** Take a peer-to-peer approach to safety orientation. For example, have someone from the plant floor or project worksite come to the class and explain the relevance of the rules. A safety person can convey a safety perspective, but if a coworker explains their perspective, people will listen. The approach shows that safety extends beyond the classroom.

4. **Test for comprehension.** Develop a test that confirms company specific expectations. The purpose of the test is not to measure intelligence. Use the test as a learning tool. A question and answer format helps people understand the expectations.

5. **Take a tour of the plant or project.** This part of orientation is easier said than done. But if you can make a point to take people on a tour of your company and point out where the safety rules apply, you will make a huge impression. Not many companies will go this extra mile. The simple action will make an impression and it will help the person feel more comfortable.

6. **Require senior level leaders to introduce themselves and express their commitment to safety.** What will a new employee remember most? Will they remember two hours of safety PowerPoints, OR will they remember when the big boss stepped into the room and talked to them about safety? They will remember that the boss took time out of his or her day to confirm the importance of safety. This interaction with the company's leader is an awesome tool for showing strategic leadership visibility.

There are multiple ways to make a positive safety impression with a new hire. You can customize your approach to meet the personality of your safety culture. The critical point to remember is to plan how you want to make the impression. Structure and organization will show people that you know how manage safety. And always remember, first impressions matter!

Practice #2: Regulatory Training - Do not take short cuts.

I have conducted audits since 1992. A training evaluation is a large component of a safety audit. Companies have to have OSHA written programs that align with the risk in their company, and they have to have regulatory training that educates the workforce on the job risks and OSHA standards. A common weakness in OSHA training is that a company will consider awareness-level training compliant for all topics. However, some topics require more extensive classes. For example, a safety orientation may include general topics such as (but not limited to) Hazard Communication, Lockout, Emergency Response, Electrical Safety, Fall Protection, Confined Space, and PPE. The awareness-level class is essential, but you cannot rely on awareness-level knowledge for all subjects.

There are two main levels to regulatory training. **1)** General topics that apply to everyone. **2)** Competent person level classes that apply to specific operations that require detailed knowledge. There are six steps to set up your training program and make is successful.

Step 1: **Assess the safety needs in your company.** Evaluate your operation and ask questions such as:

1. Has the company designated someone to coordinate safety training?
2. Has the company completed a documented training needs assessment?
3. Does the needs assessment include a comprehensive review of site-specific hazards?
4. Does the training needs assessment include: OSHA training topics required, course content, frequency of training, designated trainers, who requires what training, and testing/verification processes?

5. Does the company have an annual safety training schedule and training plan?

6. Has the company developed required safety training content and material?

7. Has the company listed designated and trained "trainers" to be used for administering safety training?

8. Does the company use trained and competent trainers for conducting safety training?

9. Does the company provide proper facilities for conducting classroom training?

10. Is the training material site specific?

11. Does the company administer documented new hire safety orientations that include OSHA required topics?

12. Does the company utilize worker participation and input for the development and delivery of safety training?

13. Does the company conduct documented practical verification and testing? (Examples include forklift, cranes, and lifts.)

14. Does the site reevaluate training program have requirements to assess new hazards?

15. Do the training attendance records outline the topic, date of training, instructor, duration, and participant names?

16. Does the company maintain the records in an organized and "auditable" fashion?

17. Does the company test, verify, and document comprehension?

18. Does the company require management to participate in safety training to show support?

19. Does the company reinforce classroom training with weekly "Toolbox" meetings?

20. Does the training include safety roles and responsibilities?

Step 2: Develop material that relates to the audience. Many companies provide comprehensive regulatory training material that includes presentations, handouts, comprehension tests, and videos. You can also get training material from OSHA's website. There is no shortage of training material on the market. Research your options, but understand that you will need to customize the material so that the class reflects your work environment. Add company-specific pictures, videos, or any other items that help an employee relate the material to what they do every day. Make sure that the material you deliver covers the details and includes methods to test comprehension, like written tests or hands-on demonstrations.

Step 3: Develop Instructors who can relate to employees. The best instructors know the material, and they also have a working knowledge of the application of the subject. Do not assign training responsibilities to someone who does not know how to do the job or task. For example, does it make sense to ask a safety professional to train people to drive a forklift if the safety professional does not know how to drive a forklift? Think about the purpose of a forklift certification program. You want the student to know how to drive a forklift, and it makes sense to use an experienced driver to perform the hands-on portion of the class. Trainers with experience and knowledge about the topic produce the best results.

Step 4: Determine how you will evaluate comprehension. Think of a test as a learning experience. When I studied for my Certified Safety Professional (CSP) exam, I tried two approaches. I read books and I took question and answer

(Q & A) practice tests. I learned more from the Q & A approach. Tests can verify what people know, but tests also teach people.

Participants need to leave the class with a thorough knowledge of the material. You can use written tests and you can use hands-on demonstrations to verify and teach. Maintain the tests and the documentation for the training in an organized fashion. Training without documentation should not occur.

Step 5: Establish an annual training schedule. Avoid last minute training at all costs. Utilize your training needs assessment to determine what classes are required. Establish a Safety Training Calendar over a 12-month period. Promote and communicate the schedule with your management team. They need to know how to plan for the classes.

Topics require refresher classes at different frequencies. As a best practice, I have always tried to schedule all applicable topics in a one-year time frame. For me, the annual approach is easier to manage.

Step 6: Get your management team involved! The mechanics and logistics of a safety training strategy are critical, but your management level of visibility and support will mean the difference between good and great. I always appreciate management involvement in two ways. Managers can show their support with a commitment to the schedule and participation in the classes. These two elements send strong messages. If managers fail to send their people to the classes, employees sense a lack of commitment. Consistency with the schedule establishes structure and expectations. When employees see managers show up at a safety class, they get the impression that the class is important. Strategic visibility sends a positive message.

In summary, develop a regulatory safety training strategy that is prepared for an audit. Align your plan with risk, OSHA written programs, and safety standards. Make sure you consider awareness level training for the masses and schedule classes for competent person training. Document the training and maintain the paperwork in an organized manner. If you manage these elements and get managers involved, your strategy will experience success.

Practice #3: Safety Leadership Training - 10 Safe Habits

Does your company put people in roles with inadequate preparation to lead safety? I have witnessed great employees who get a promotion to a supervisor role and then struggle to lead the safety aspect of the job. They understand the technical nature of the supervisor role, but they do not know how to lead people to work safely. They have the desire to prevent injuries, but they do not know how to accomplish that goal.

Safety Leadership Training should teach tactical skills that supervisors can use to prevent injuries. Managers and supervisors should learn to approach others, deliver a safety topic, train workers, mentor new employees, preplan work, benefit from lessons learned, identify hazards, evaluate events, and hold people accountable. That may sound like a fairy tale list of skills, but it is possible if we deliver Safety Leadership Training that cultivates these critical skills.

What should a class look like?

Safety Leadership Training Content - 10 Safe Habit Tools

1. **Approaching Others** – Include a module that highlights the value of hazard recognition and the importance of saying something when you see risk. You would think this basic skill comes naturally to people, but it is not natural. We have to develop an Approaching Others mentality with managers and supervisors.

2. **Deliver Good Toolbox Topics** – Take advantage of standard weekly safety meetings and communicate safety messages on a consistent basis. Teach people how to deliver a good safety topic and you will raise situational awareness. To keep a group's attention, you have to have a good delivery.

3. **Training and Development** – Training does not just happen. A manager and supervisor have to know what workers in training need, and when they need it. Leaders have to understand how critical their support and visibility is to the success of the training. And they have to reinforce what people learn.

4. **Mentor New Employees** – Good leaders are approachable, and they coach people in the field. Teach managers and supervisors how to mentor new employees. Explain how they can set up and execute a new hire mentoring program. Create a learning environment.

5. **Preplan Your Work** – Plan your work and work your plan. The best leaders understand this principle and how it applies to safety. Teach managers and supervisors to create effective prejob briefs. They need to plan their steps, anticipate errors, think about the worst case, and put controls in place.

6. **Post Job Reviews** (Lessons Learned) – A good plan is important, but events may not always go as planned. Teach managers and supervisors to learn from mistakes. Show them

how to implement a simple review process at the end of the shift so that they can talk about what went right and what went wrong. The recap will help the team perform better the next day.

7. **Audit and Inspect** – Audits teach people expectations. Every manager and supervisor should know how to audit and inspect their areas of responsibility. Teach them good hazard recognition skills so that they see what you want them to see. Give them the tools to implement a documented weekly safety audit plan.

8. **Event Analysis** – Teach managers and supervisors how to analyze events that have the potential to cause injuries. The goal is to learn what tools and techniques failed, so that the leaders can make improvements. The improvements should influence the future in a positive way.

9. **Hold People Accountable** – Accountability is the best teacher. This is a manager and supervisor's greatest tool and responsibility. They need to know the importance of disciplinary action and how to hold people accountable. Safety Leadership Training should make this point clear.

10. **PEAK Safety Dialogue** – This a preplanning tool designed to get people engaged in safety by promoting personal preplanning and error prevention techniques. The process encourages people to ask questions about planning critical steps, evaluating risk, anticipating mistakes, and knowing the controls.

How do you build safe habits?

You can cultivate these 10 skills with training, but how do you make these skills a habit that is ingrained into your daily routines? Charles Duhigg wrote a book called *The Power of Habit*. In his book, he states that "new habits are created by putting together a cue, a routine, and a reward." This habit loop creates a natural craving to repeat the activity. The habit loop has the power to influence safe decisions, and it will have a positive impact on our judgment.

Teach managers and supervisors to apply safe habit tools at the right times. Develop the expectation to apply these tools whenever leaders encounter certain triggers and cues. Promote the value and reward of the techniques, and apply them with repetition. This process takes extra focus in the beginning, but after people get used to the routine, these techniques become second nature (aka a safe habit).

For example, here are 10 safe habits that improve safety performance:

Tool & Technique	Trigger/Cue	Routine	Reward
Approach Others	Anticipated Hazard	Minute by Minute	Injury Prevention
Tool Box Topics	Upcoming Work	Weekly	Situational Awareness
Train and Develop	Starting the Job	Before the Need	More Knowledge
Mentoring	New Hire	First 90 Days	Better Skills
Prejob Brief	Before You Start	Daily	Fewer Mistakes
Post Review (LL)	End of the Day	Daily	Better Plan Tomorrow
Audit and Inspect	Starting the Job	Daily	Fewer Hazards
Event Analysis	Event Occurrence	As Needed	Learn from Mistakes
Disciplinary Action	Noncompliance	As Needed	Accountability
PEAK Safety Dialogue	Before Critical Task	Daily	Better Planning and Error Reduction

Safety Leadership Training is like your GPS. You have a starting point and you have your desired destination. To reach the destination (safe culture), you have to follow the blue line. Each safe habit you develop with your supervisors is a marker on the blue line. Once you develop these ten habits, you reach the safe culture destination.

Your goal is to prepare people to lead safety so that they do not struggle to prevent injuries. Supervisors know the technical nature of their jobs, and we have to help them understand how safe habits impact the details of their work. Build these ten safe habit tools into their work activities and you will improve their opportunity to succeed. Safety leadership is all about influence and what better way to influence safe actions! [5]

Practice #4: Communicate Safety Like a Fan

Lack of communication is a trap that will limit success. Have you ever sent an email about a subject and considered your communication complete, but then nothing happened? Have you ever written a procedure, added it to your management system, but then realized that no one actually follows the procedure? Have you ever created a safety campaign, emailed it to your team, but later found out that the workers never heard about it? Have you ever had thoughts like, "They should know," "We told them," and "That is our policy"? If you have had these experiences, you have fallen into the lack of communication trap and I am guilty as well.

When safety communication is one dimensional, we limit our potential. Communicate your safety interest with relentless passion. Surround people with your safety message. Develop safe habits with memorable and methodical communications. Employees need to know safety is important because they see and hear a consistent and relentless message.

---

5. *PSJ Professional Safety*, January 2020, assp.org

Think about how we communicate interest to people around us. For example, sports fans know how to communicate their interest. In my house, the universe revolves around football. My enthusiasm for football began when I was young. My earliest memories include going to Friday night high school football games and watching football on television all weekend. Following football is a tradition that continues today. Our house is consumed with a message that football is vital to our existence.

I acquired my enthusiasm from multiple influences. I have personal experience with football. My dad, brother, and I all played football in college. My dad also coached high school football. There is also a fan side to the story. We watch football on television. There is an anticipation side of the equation: I look forward to football and count the days until it begins. There is an awareness element: we talk about football constantly. There is a visible side to our obsession: we wear our team's colors and purchase "stuff" with our team's logo. There is an educational side, too: we read articles and books about football teams and players. And there is a financial commitment to our message: the games, tickets, equipment, and promotional material all cost money.

If you did not know my family, how long would it take you to determine that we like football? Not long! We communicate our enthusiasm for the sport with our words, our actions, our time, and our money. It is not a strategic communication campaign, but rather a natural product of our interest. The influence carries over to my three boys. They all played football. I wonder where they acquired their interest. Was it random chance? No, of course not – sports fans *communicate* their interest in the sport.

Apply the same principle to your safety culture. If safety is vital to your existence, you have to communicate it through every possible avenue. Your interest, enthusiasm, confidence, and sincerity will become evident to everyone. Your goal is to instill dedication and commitment into your program with a sustained effort to pump your message into your work environment. Let your world revolve around safety.

Effective communication will come from seven different directions. That could mean seven different people, seven different communication mediums, or seven different training sessions. The idea is to present the message with repetition, enthusiasm, and confidence. Show your passion for safety and sustain the message. Keep it simple but methodical. Also realize that communication is more than simply an email stating a few goals. Your attitude, confidence, and enthusiasm will communicate what is important to you.

Communication Methods

Visual: Become safety's biggest fan and make it obvious. Employees should see your injury-free culture everywhere with banners, posters, flags, flyers, letterhead, giveaways, hats, shirts, jackets, bulletin boards, and any other conceivable method to make safety visible. Brand your message with symbols and logos. Keep the message consistent, but change the format frequently.

Verbal: Employees should hear the message from multiple directions. Every member of your leadership team should talk about your message in their sleep. Your workforce will begin to expect the first words out of your mouth will always be safety-related. Integrate the spoken word into your environment. Talk to people. Show people safety-related information. Require a safety topic before ALL meetings. Develop the ability to ask good safety-related questions. Create an environment that discusses safety informally.

Written Messages: Communicate with newsletters, memos, letters to employees, brochures, and flyers. There are endless ways to put your message into the hands of employees. Keep your communication simple, and focused like a laser on your core messages. Every written document you produce should have a reference to safety – or, at a minimum, it should incorporate your safety logo or symbol. Communicate your expectations, goals, and responsibilities. Have people sign documents conveying their commitment. Use technology to put the written word out there through web sites, emails, blogs, Twitter, and Facebook. You name it - you can do it. I even know of one site that posts their safety and health newsletter on the inside of the toilet stall doors! Their newsletter is aptly titled, *The Porcelain Press.*

Informal Communication: Your conversations count. Safety is not relegated to a formal safety meeting. People know what is important to you by the content of your questions and conversations. Talk about safety when you eat. Talk about safety when you meet. Talk about safety at the coffee pot. Talk about safety on breaks. Talk about safety outside of work. Talk about safety with your family. Relive accomplishments. The idea is to make safety a topic of every conversation, just like a sports fan talks about his favorite team.

Safety communication is like cable television – you have to have the "Headline News" version of your message as well as the one-hour documentary version. Both approaches will appeal to different people at different times. Cable stations report on the same events, but each network has its own style. Your average viewer cruises the channels sampling different perspectives on the same current events. Take the same approach with your communications and awareness campaigns. Deliver the same core messages using multiple networks. Your safety commitment is not a secret. You create safety fans with a demonstration of your own passion for what is important to you! The benefit is that your safety culture will spread.

Practice #5: The Power of a Safety Topic

Every company has to have consistent methods for communication. Get your common messages out to the people. Consistent Safety Topic Meetings (or messages) is one way to keep safety in front of people. You can deliver topics once a week, every day, or you can give a topic talk before every meeting. The goal is to provide a vehicle to promote common messages that will keep people safe.

Safety "Moment" before a Meeting

While I worked at Fluor, I helped lead a corporate initiative to attain OSHA's Voluntary Protection Program (VPP) Corporate Star status. When the federal OSHA VPP assessment team spent the week at our corporate office in Greenville, South Carolina, they interviewed a lot of people. One of the main questions they asked was, "Can you give examples of how Fluor demonstrates a strong safety culture?" There was one overwhelming response that was consistent in the interviews. Employees described how Fluor started every meeting of three or more people with a safety topic.

When the OSHA representatives first told me that was the overwhelming answer that they received in their interviews, I was initially disappointed. I thought to myself, "We do SO many things to promote our safety culture, and the one thing people remember most is a safety topic before meetings?" I was puzzled as to why that made such an impression. Don't get me wrong, the safety topics before each meeting helped build the culture. But I did not know what made the process so impressionable. After a lot of reflection, I came to the conclusion that Fluor had created a cultural "icon." No matter where you went around the world, Fluor employees were accustomed to hearing a safety topic before each meeting. It was a universal process that communicated more than just content. The commitment to incorporate safety into thousands of meetings around the world made a cultural impression on Fluor employees. Safety is important!

Weekly Safety Meetings

Have you have ever sat through a meeting where a supervisor read a couple of pages about a topic and never looked up or changed their tone of voice? The only thing you remember about the meeting was how boring it was. Once you have established your expectation, you will need to develop people's skills so that they can give a good topic. The most memorable topics are relevant and personal. Here are ten tips that can help anyone give a better safety topic:

Ten Tips for Making Your Talk Memorable

1. Do not read the talking points. Know the subject and speak with your own voice.
2. Show examples: pictures, videos, site specific props, or point out something on the job site.
3. Make the topic vivid with a story by sharing a personal example of how the topic applies.
4. Talk about positive examples of how to apply your talking points.
5. Help people visualize the consequences. Share examples of related injuries.
6. Create "triggers" that will prompt people to think about the topics throughout the day.
7. Use humor in your discussion with pictures, videos, or cartoons.
8. Your job is to get people to imagine, think, and feel the value of the talking points.
9. Be interesting. Your audience will not forgive you for being boring.
10. Encourage people to ask good questions.

Your company has an opportunity to create a safety "icon" with safety topics. The key is to integrate your message into the daily life of every employee. Here are a few steps to consider:

1. Evaluate the risk at your company.
2. Choose safety topics that address the risk.
3. Define how often you will have a Safety Topic (weekly, daily, or before meetings.)
4. Assign responsibility to people who will give the topics.
5. Provide guidance on how to deliver a great safety topic.
6. Track participation and hold people accountable.
7. Document who delivered the topic, describe the subject, and record who was present.
8. Make the process a cultural icon that everyone expects and respects.

A structured, consistent, and vivid communication approach will build cultural icons in your company. Cultures rely on the collective influence of every individual who participates in the process. I challenge you to champion the cause and dedicate your efforts to deliver the best Safety Topic Meetings. Your commitment today influences tomorrow's results!

Principle 3 Summary: Safety Training and Communication

Who learns more – the teacher or the student? I remember one of the first training classes that I had to present to a group of supervisors and managers. The purpose of the class was to explain a new safety team structure that we were adopting at our plant. I did not have experience speaking in public, and I was nervous. To compensate for my anxiety, I spent several hours in preparation. I did not want to make any mistakes, and I learned every detail of the material we were presenting. I wanted to have the answers to all the questions.

I was the teacher, but I learned more than the students because of how much I prepared. Think about what your organization will look like when leaders take on a role where they know they have to teach people how to work safely. Expect your leaders to teach, and provide them with the structure to do so. This format will help develop a learning culture where everyone benefits. Leadership training, follow-up through coaching, and constant communication offer the vehicles to promote a learning culture.

I want you to have the confidence to build a safety training framework that is more than a collection of safety PowerPoints. Develop and implement five practices that demonstrate a learning culture. A focus on basic regulatory training schedules, safety leadership training, safety toolbox topics, and communication strategies will help put your learning culture in motion. With the right character, mentality, and results focus, you will make a difference!

PRINCIPLE 4
Introduction to Worksite Analysis

The hardest sell in the safety profession is to convince people to enjoy a safety audit. However, a strong audit culture impacts safety performance because it requires you to measure your effectiveness and learn from the findings. The key word is to LEARN. When you analyze your capacity to lead safety, you establish a set of shared attitudes, values, goals, practices, and expectations that characterize your company or corporation.

It is easy to say audits, assessments, analysis tools, and investigations are great learning tools, but when you are the subject of the audit or investigation, the process is not comfortable. For example, when I worked at Duracell, the VP of corporate safety decided to host a one-week auditing seminar with 25 Duracell safety professionals. My facility in Lancaster, South Carolina, where we made over one billion batteries a year, was the host site for the seminar. Our plant had a fast-paced environment with a high demand for production. The goal for the corporate safety class was to teach people how to audit, and they wanted to use our facility as the site for the hands-on "group exercise." Who would want to volunteer for that "learning" experience?

You can imagine what my week was like as I accommodated 25 eager safety professionals looking for noncompliance safety issues to present in the classroom portion of the workshop. I had to answer everyone's questions. I had to explain processes, provide documentation, coordinate plant tours, walk through training, arrange interviews, and "learn" from the experience with a smile on my face. When you are under that type of pressure, you do not feel the value of external help. I felt defensive and almost persecuted, even though my professional colleagues were there to help.

I survived the stressful week. After I recovered from the trauma, I realized that a fresh set of eyes provided enormous value to our improvement process. The experience is a lot like going to the doctor for an annual exam. The visit is not fun, but the exercise is critical to your health and well-being. Audits are the same. You get through the experience with greater knowledge and more focus on how to make your company safer.

Audits are one way that you evaluate safety, but there are others processes that you should introduce to create a strong safety culture. For Principle 4, readers will learn five practices that demonstrate how to incorporate worksite analysis into your culture. The processes will promote the value of learning and improvement. The goal is to provide examples for how you can make your analysis processes more effective. The focus is on audits, event analysis, pretask planning, equipment inspections, and trend analysis. Your mission is to evaluate how well your company implements these practices. Look for areas where you can improve, and put a plan in place to make it happen. With the right character, mentality, and results focus, you will make a difference!

Practice #1: Learn from Your Audits

Audits are tools for each party to learn a different safety perspective. A culture that learns from the process impacts safety performance because it requires you to measure your effectiveness, implement corrective actions, and teach hazard identification skills. When you analyze your work, you can align shared attitudes, values, goals, and practices of your company in order to keep workers safe.

An audit can intimidate you no matter on what side of the fence you stand. I remember my first job after I graduated from college. I was amazed at how people became so nervous when I introduced myself. I was only 23 years old – how could I intimidate people? I guess they were nervous because I was an OSHA Compliance Officer. After all, doesn't everyone want an unannounced visitor from the Department of Labor?

The irony of my job with OSHA is that I was 10 times more nervous than the people I inspected. I do not like to identify a stranger's problems. After 200 inspections, the nervousness never went away. Even though the anxiety never subsided, I became more confident in my job because I learned the OSHA standards and how they applied. I learned how to interact with people and answer their questions with self-assurance. When I did not have the answer, I knew where to go.

Overall, the experience and repetition made my job easier, and it created an "auditing mindset" that extended beyond work. For example, when I ride down the road and see a job site, I audit everything I can see. My wife and three boys have gotten used to it. They will tell me, "Yeah Dad, I know. They're not tied off!" Audits create a mindset and a culture that identifies risk.

As your audit program matures, you will see participants gain confidence with experience and repetition. They will adopt an observant perspective that will mold your culture. Listed below are six elements that will make your field audit program successful:

1. **Participation is vital.** Anyone who supervises or directs employees should conduct audits that are appropriate for their area of responsibility. When leaders support the audit program with their participation, they instill a sense of urgency in the program, and their presence should drive corrective action.

2. **Audit frequently.** Participants should perform audits every week. There is more value in frequent short audits than long, drawn out audits, because people accumulate expectations. They know if you look for risk on a regular basis, it prompts them to prepare. If you audit less frequently, preparation is less frequent. The bigger the risk, the more you should be assessing it.

3. **Participants have to develop confidence with their audits.** Leaders drive the success of the audit program with the confidence in their ability to identify and correct safety observations. When I started with OSHA, I was nervous for two reasons: 1) I did not know what to look for in most environments. 2) I have a reserved personality. I overcame both obstacles with experience. Coach and encourage participants and allow them the opportunity to learn how to identify risk and confront the issues.

4. **Identify standards to which you will audit.** What if OSHA did not audit to a preselected set of standards? What if OSHA had the authority to make rules up as they go from site to site? As the one being audited, you would never know how to prepare. So give people an opportunity to succeed. Tell them what you will look for each time you conduct an audit.

5. **Follow through with corrective actions.** Document all observations. Be sure you have explained clearly what the issues and non-compliances are; then monitor the corrective actions. Keep in mind that long-term true corrective actions eliminate hazards. If you correct it today and it resurfaces tomorrow, was it really corrected?

6. **Hold leaders accountable!** If you expect a certain level of performance, do not let people perform less without consequences. Record, track, and eliminate repeat observations, and then reward those who do well. A good audit program is a great tool to see who has what it takes to influence and lead. If an employee cannot manage safety, then he or she cannot manage the rest of the business effectively.

As you develop your audit program, establish responsibilities such as:

		Frequency	Responsibility
1	Conduct a scored audit.	Weekly	Manager and Supervisor
2	Track observations to completion.	Weekly	Manager and Supervisor
3	Track and Trend repeat observations	Weekly	Manager
4	Hold people accountable for repeat items.	Daily	Managers
5	Incorporate results into individual performance reviews.	Annually	Managers

An effective audit program will have a monumental impact on your culture. Provide training to support hazard identification. Establish expectations for participation. Track participation and hold people accountable for the results. You will experience the secret to success when participants adopt an attitude that accepts each analysis as an opportunity to learn and improve. As you develop your audit program, participants will gain confidence with experience and repetition.

Practice #2: CONTEXT Root Cause Analysis

I know what it is like to get injured on the job. When I was 18 years old, I worked as summer help for a small contractor in industrial environments. I did what I was told. During this particular summer, we worked at a textile mill in South Carolina. My supervisor asked me to move some platform grating from inside the plant to the back of the plant.

The grating was heavy, awkward, and unstable, but I loaded it onto the hand truck anyway. As I transported the load through the plant, I bounced over uneven surfaces, and the grating started to fall. I reacted and tried to stabilize the load by placing my right hand between two sheets of grating. The pinch point lacerated the top of my hand, and I looked down to see my tendons and veins. Five stitches later, I became an OSHA-recordable injury.

As a safety professional, I know the frustration you feel when you analyze an event like my injury. The two ends of the spectrum provide unique insight. I look at my past injury and ask, "What was I thinking?" But when I was 18 years old, everything I did leading up to the incident made perfect sense.

As a safety professional, I have learned there is value in context because it can help you focus on influencing future decisions. These four steps can help put an event into context.

Step 1: Start with the Storyboard. Map the critical steps that led to the event. Explain what happened that day.

1) I reported to work.
2) We traveled to the work site from the company office.
3) My supervisor told me to move the platform grating.
4) I found a hand truck and loaded multiple pieces of grating.
5) I transported the grating through the mill.
6) The sheets became unstable.
7) I tried to grab the grating and pinched my hand, causing a laceration that required stitches.

Do we have all of the information we need to prevent similar incidents from happening in the future? I have witnessed work cultures that accept similar timelines as sufficient information to complete a report. They put the blame on the employee and continue with their day. Blame is quick and easy. When you take the "individual blame" approach, you fail to recognize that someone else may make the same choice in the future. How are you going to influence the next person?

Step 2: Build Context. The storyboard is a critical first step that gives you a factual timeline for the event. It does not explain what the injured person thought at the time of the incident. The context of the event describes why it made sense to perform that task, and also the details associated with each critical step of the day. What did the context look like?

I worked for a small company that did not have any safety training, nor a structured safety program. We did not have specific rules to follow. We were not required to wear gloves. There was no formal preplanning nor prejob briefs. No one ever mentioned safety. We simply performed basic contract work and never thought about getting hurt.

When you are inexperienced, you may be assigned the jobs that no one else wants to do. I did what I was told and I did not ask questions. I had minimal direction, oversight, and experience. The morning that I got hurt was a normal day. My supervisor asked me to "clean up and move some platform grating," which was the extent of my instructions. The sheets were heavy and awkward, but I thought I could move all four sheets at once with the hand truck. That made logical sense because I did not want to take more than one trip to move the grating.

My supervisor did not provide specific instructions, so I proceeded with my plan. I took the most direct route through the plant without consideration for the uneven surfaces and the unstable load. I did not anticipate the load would shift, and I never thought I could get hurt. I was confident that I could accomplish this task in one trip, and there was no one around to provide safer direction. If I were performing an event analysis today, what would I learn?

Step 3: Analyze the Facts.

The Individual: The fact is that I overloaded the hand truck to save time. I did not consider the safest route to take the grating, and I did not have a last line of defense: gloves. I did not anticipate any mistakes, and I did not think I would get hurt. My decisions led to my injury. Would you conclude your analysis with these facts?

Tip: If the focus is on the individual, your impact on

sustainable improvement is limited to that one person. Is that the goal?

The Organization: The fact is that my supervisor did not conduct any type of prejob safety brief. He did not give specific instructions, and he did not monitor my work. There were no formal safety rules, safety training, safety toolbox topics, safety audits, or general safety communications. I was inexperienced, and my supervisor expected me to learn on my own. What responsibility does a supervisor have in this situation? Should a company have tools and techniques that help an inexperienced worker perform their job safely?

Tip: To drive sustainable improvement for more than one person, organizations must identify tools and techniques that will produce safe decisions and judgement.

Step 4: Choose Points of Influence. Where do you have the most influence? How can leaders in an organization take inexperienced workers and help them make good decisions? Based on the individual and the organizational facts, look for points of influence that impact decisions and judgement in the future.

General Influence

- ○ Establish the tone of the safety culture with basic safety training required by OSHA.
- ○ Conduct weekly safety meetings that reaffirm safety requirements.
- ○ Teach supervisors and workers the importance of preplanning safety into every task.
- ○ Talk about hazard identification and risk reduction in the workplace.

These general requirements may not have a direct impact on my injury, but the safety culture can influence how we make decisions. The absence of these critical elements in a safety program will have an overall impact on safety results.

Specific Influence

- ○ Conduct a prejob safety brief before each shift. Cover critical steps, hazards, and controls.
- ○ Monitor safe work practices with safety audits and walk-throughs.
- ○ Coach and mentor employees who do not have experience.
- ○ Implement work-critical safety rules and guidelines such as the use of proper PPE.

The benefit of an intuitive root cause analysis process is that it improves organizational tools and techniques that prevent errors in judgement that lead to injuries. The context of the storyboard provides insight to a supervisor because he or she can choose points of future influence using the right tools. Prejob safety briefs, audits, coaching, and basic rules are tactical tools that a supervisor could have used in my situation.

Conclusion

Clearly, I made some bad choices and I own the results. The owner held me responsible for my actions, and I did not make the same mistake again. The problem was solved, right? Do not forget that when people get hurt, the decisions they made at the time of the injury made sense. There was a reason I made the choices that led to the injury. If one person made that choice, others will certainly do the same without the right tools and techniques to mold their judgement.

The goal in an event analysis is to create a storyboard that describes the context of the event with facts, not fault. If we know what motivated the decisions that caused the injury, we can initiate a plan to influence the future with all employees who may fall into the same trap. This plan impacts more than just the person who was injured; it impacts the whole organization.[6]

Practice #3: Plan Your Work and Work Your Plan

More than once, I have heard people make these comments after an injury. Better yet, I have made the same comments after an injury. "I knew better." "What was I thinking?" "That was not smart!" Nobody plans to get hurt. We have to PLAN not to get hurt. Consider this scenario.

Example: You receive a maintenance request to change lights in a conference room. You get your tools, materials, and ladder, and you proceed to change the lights. Once you get to the conference room, you realize that you brought the 6-foot ladder but you really need an 8-foot ladder. To get the right ladder will take an extra fifteen minutes to do an easy job. You realize that if you stand on the top rung of the ladder, you can get the job done immediately. You have a decision: Either do the job faster with more risk, or take your time and get the right ladder. What would you be tempted to do? Post a lookout and hope no one sees you on the top rung of the ladder?

If you fell, how would your organization look at the incident? Is this a simple injury that resulted from a failure to follow the rules? Or is the real problem that you did not have an effective plan with the correct sized ladder. A good plan will set you up for success. A good plan will minimize the decisions that lead to injuries.

Good safety planning is a discipline that you should integrate

6.   *PSJ Professional Safety,* August 2018, assp.org

into three phases of work. An effective plan requires people to think before they act; an effective plan will also identify the risks and identify appropriate actions to mitigate hazards. This section will help you develop tools that encourage crews to evaluate every step of their day, so they can consider the risk and the proper way to mitigate the hazards.

Job Safety Analysis (JSA)

A JSA evaluates a job (a series of tasks) in its entirety. This analysis is a big picture tool. You can evaluate each step in a job and identify the hazards associated with each step. Once you know the hazards, you can put defenses in place to protect people. A JSA allows you to think through the job as a whole and prepare for individual steps. You perform a JSA before you begin a project. It is similar to a work procedure that identifies risks throughout the procedure. Leaders should use a team approach to develop the JSA. The more input you get from different perspectives, the more effective the JSA tool is.

What makes a great JSA program?

1. Develop a priority list for what jobs will require a JSA.
2. Get the people who do the job to help develop the JSA.
3. Update the JSAs when the job changes, or when you discover additional risk.
4. Ask great "What if?" questions.
5. Review JSAs with employees on a periodic basis.
6. Audit compliance with the JSAs.

Pretask Plan (PTP)

A PTP focuses on the risk associated with a specific task for that day. Identify all potential hazards in the work environment. Use the PTP to remind your team of the required permits, PPE, training qualifications, and other miscellaneous safety precautions associated with a specific task for the day. A supervisor should perform a PTP with their crew every morning before employees start work. The crew should use this time as a prejob brief for the day. Have each employee sign the PTP at the start of the shift. Following the completion of the task, or at the end of the day, conduct a post-task briefing. The supervisor should document all concerns or incidents that happened that day. Have each employee initial the PTP during the post-shift PTP brief, indicating their agreement with all items on the PTP.

What makes a great PTP program?

1. The supervisor walks down the job before the day begins to observe potential hazards.
2. The PTP is complete with comprehensive details for steps, hazards, and prevention.
3. The supervisor gets employees involved with the PTP when they deliver the message.
4. Employees provide feedback and relate to personal experiences.
5. The crews start a new PTP if the work scope changes.
6. The supervisor completes a post-job review to discuss lessons learned.
7. Everyone signs the PTP at the beginning and end of the shift.
8. You know it is a good PTP if employees can tell you what they discussed.
9. Senior managers attend to show support.

Last Minute Risk Assessment (LMRA)

Injuries happen fast based on split-second decisions. An LMRA is designed to prompt good individual decisions at the task level.

This discipline will minimize errors that lead to injuries. The process starts with a series of simple questions and safe responses.

Questions:

1. What could go wrong?
2. How bad could it be?
3. Has anything changed?
4. Am I physically ready?
5. Am I mentally ready?
6. Do I understand my task?
7. Do I have the right tools?
8. Do I have the right equipment?

Response:

- Make it safe – Ask for help.
- Use the right procedure.
- Use the right tool.
- Reduce the risk.

What makes a great LMRA program?

1. Develop a campaign with long-term consistent promotions.
2. Give employees reminder cards with LMRA questions.
3. Talk about LMRAs every day.
4. Ask employees every day if they did an LMRA before their task.
5. Ingrain the process into every thought and task.

Plan your work and work your plan! Measure twice and cut once! Every facet of your business will benefit from a good plan. Think about the earlier scenario. What if there was a Job Safety

Analysis for changing lights or using a ladder? What if the supervisor reviewed the proper tools and materials required for the job? And what if the employee reviewed the job and asked Last Minute Risk Assessment questions? A layered safety planning process will impact the safety outcome. It is a cornerstone to safety success.

Practice #4: Inspect Everything

Have you ever conducted an audit and observed a missing ground pin on an extension cord, a frayed web sling, a damaged safety harness, a label missing on a ladder, a fire extinguisher without a charge, a missing guard on a grinder, or poor housekeeping? If you have detected these noncompliance items in an audit, I bet this thought passed through your mind. How many times did the user or supervisor have the opportunity to see the issue before I did?

The answer is simple. People do not believe anything will ever happen, even if the items are not compliant. Employees take chances because they trust that the equipment will not fail. Everything will work as it is supposed to work. Our overconfidence leads to complacency. The users and supervisors do not always take it seriously because they do not connect the potential reality of the risk with their actions. They think to themselves, "It is not a big deal."

However, my goal is to set up systems that encourage and expect the user and supervisor to find these noncompliance issues before you do.

The "Layered" Process:
Layer One (informal):

- Observe the condition of your tools and equipment.

- The user is required to inspect the equipment before use.

- If there is a problem, the user is required to take it out of service or correct the problem.

- The supervisor is responsible for compliance.

Layer Two (formal):

- Identify competent people to perform documented periodic inspections. (The competent person needs to have the appropriate knowledge and experience that allows them to identify the hazard. They have to have the authority to correct the problem.)

- Keep a record of who are your competent people. Maintain training records and other credentials that support their competence.

- Define the requirements. What will you inspect and how often? At a minimum, inspect the following tools and equipment; 1) electrical cords and plugs; 2) ladders; 3) rigging equipment; 4) fire extinguishers; 5) electrical PPE; 6) mobile equipment; 7) fall protection equipment; 8) scaffolds.

- Documentation Options: 1) Keep a record of inspections on a spreadsheet. 2) Utilize tags on the equipment to verify the last inspection date. 3) Use a color-coded system. Designate a color for each month. Once you inspect the tool, place electrical tape with the chosen color for the month on the piece of equipment. You can also color-code methods such as tie wraps or stickers. Use what makes sense for your organization.

Layer Three:

- A safety professional should perform periodic inspections.

The safety professional is the last line of defense. Establish structure in your inspection system so that you can hold the user and the supervisor accountable for noncompliance issues related to inadequate inspections.

Think about the importance of a comprehensive inspection system for tools and equipment. How important would you rate the layered inspection process in this scenario? When I was 46 years old, I decided that I wanted to tandem skydive. The event required multiple layers of inspections. Designated company representatives (competent people) followed formal inspection processes for the equipment. The person that jumped with me (supervisor), inspected my equipment while we were on the ground. He also inspected my equipment while we were on the plane. I (the user) also frantically inspected my equipment throughout the entire experience to make sure that everything was connected.

Why was a layered inspection process important to my skydiving adventure? It was important because an equipment failure would have produced an imminent result! Death was certain if something went wrong. When you jump out of a plane, you want every piece of life-saving equipment to work without fail, and therefore multiple inspections make sense.

How do you translate skydiving to work-related safety? What happens if your rigging equipment breaks while you are lifting a heavy load? What happens if you pick up an energized inspection cord with a fray? What happens if you climb an unstable ladder? Or what if your electrical PPE has a hole in it? All of these "What if?" scenarios can have an imminent outcome as well. Work hard to convince your team that inspections are more than just an OSHA compliance activity. Inspections are a lifesaving necessity, and the user gains the benefit!

Practice #5: Top 5 Trends to Analyze

I heard a college football coach, Will Muschamp, make an interesting comment about statistics during an interview. He ranted about how the media likes to keep track of statistics that do not have a direct impact on winning games. Coach Muschamp stated, "There are five statistical categories that are critical to winning ballgames: turnover margin, explosive plays, field position, winning the fourth quarter, and red zone success." His point was that there is a statistic for everything in sports, but you have to narrow your focus to only the critical trends that make a real difference.

What statistics make a real difference in the safety world? When I look at a chart with safety data, I want to have a vision for my next step. I want the chart to prompt clear action that drives safety improvement in a specific area. Not all data will give you critical "winning" clarity. Some trends are just informational. For example, if you have a trend with hand safety, do you really have a clear next step? If you have a trend with lacerations, do you really know what you need to do next? If your recordable rate is trending down, does that really describe your safety culture? These informational statistics make good charts and they prompt broad generic responses. They are the media talking points version of safety statistics.

I want tactical trends that provide a focus on my next step. I want to see trends that point me to triggers that lead to injuries. If I know the triggers, I can develop safe habits that minimize the risk. What statistical categories are critical to winning at safety?

Top 5 Trends with Action:

1. **Action or Task** – Track the action or task that people are engaged in when negative events happen. This information is the most important element that you can track because you can observe the common activities that

people perform that could produce injuries. To respond, you develop safe habits that address high accident potential activities. Here are common examples:

    a. Moving materials – You can pinch fingers or strain a muscle.

    b. Using cutting utensils – You can cut yourself.

    c. Walking or traveling – You can slip, trip, and fall.

    d. Operating tools – Tools can cause a variety of injuries.

    e. Clearing jams – Your fingers are at risk when you clear jams.

    f. Chemical handling – Exposure can cause burns.

    g. Welding and grinding – You can get burned and you can get particles in your eyes.

2. **Root Causes** – A root cause is an initial condition or action that leads to an event. What is the trigger that set the event in motion, or influenced the outcome? If you know the common root causes, you can anticipate the future and make improvements. Here are five common root causes that will lead to an injury:

    a. Poor Planning

    b. Inadequate Hazard Recognition

    c. Inadequate Training

    d. Poor Communication

    e. Risk Tolerance

3. **System Failure** –Your systems serve as a defense or barrier that separates people from the hazards. A system failure means one of your defenses or barriers did not work. Here are common systems failures that can lead to injuries:

    a. Incomplete Prejob Brief

    b. Inadequate Safety Audit/Inspection

    c. Poor Safety Topic Delivery

    d. Inadequate Hazard Recognition Training

    e. No Last-Minute Risk Assessment

4. **Error-Likely Situation** – We all make mistakes and mistakes are predictable! The key is to track the most common error precursors that lead to injuries with your company. If you know these precursors, you can focus your injury prevention strategy on these elements. Here are five common examples:

    a. Time and Pressure

    b. Distractions

    c. Complacency

    d. Inexperience

    e. Stress

5. **Supervisor or Manager** – Leadership is the key to risk management, and safety is a performance measure just like quality, cost, and schedule. If trends lead to a specific supervisor or manager, you have an opportunity to address accountability for safety. Supervisors and Managers have to produce safety results. Here are examples of leadership failures that lead to injuries:

    a. Inadequate participation with safety audits

    b. Inadequate participation with safety topics

    c. Inadequate participation with pretask plans

    d. Poor hazard recognition

    e. Slow corrective action

Informational statistics have a place in safety, but do not limit your success to a focus on general facts. Identify statistical categories that are critical to winning with safety. Look for your critical trends with injuries. Consider critical trends with audits. What are your trends with company safety systems? Your focus on critical categories will provided vision for you next step. Your charts will prompt clear actions that drive safety improvement in a specific area.

Principle 4 Summary – Worksite Analysis

Organizations have to evaluate their safety processes, identify risk, inspect the equipment, integrate safety into preplanning, and analyze events. It is a simple principle with a monumental impact on injury reduction. A thorough system for worksite analysis also develops safety awareness in the individuals who perform the audits, assessments, and analysis. Safety awareness helps leaders prevent injuries, and also helps an organization mature.

When I worked at Fluor, we had an aggressive injury reporting protocol that included requirements for notification, analysis, and executive review. When someone had an injury that required medical treatment, the site had to report the event to their corporate leadership. Within three days, they had to coordinate a conference call with the business line executives to explain what happened and they had to report on the corrective action. The expectation generated focus on a detailed root cause analysis for the event. Project Managers had to be prepared to answer any potential questions on the call. Executives did not respond well to poor preparation, because it showed a lack of safety commitment. The calls were stressful for project representatives, but the scrutiny prompted learning. The analysis generated positive change. The point is that a structured analysis process with the proper level of support from a leadership team drives positive results in a safety culture.

There are obvious benefits. If an audit is on the schedule, the recipient will prepare. If a comprehensive event analysis is an expectation, leaders will respond with a thorough approach. If leaders follow key safety trends, the problems get more attention.

Every party in the process learns from each experience and they adjust. Readers learned five practices that demonstrate how to implement worksite analysis into your culture. The goal is to provide examples for how you can make your analysis processes more effective. Look for areas where you can improve, and put a plan in place to make it happen. With the right character, mentality, and results in focus, you will make a difference!

PRINCIPLE 5
Injury Prevention and Control

Companies that have exceptional safety cultures share common characteristics. They understand fundamental safety principles, and they execute them through methodical prevention and control practices. There are almost limitless ways to prevent hazards and control risk. The key is to identify the greatest potential for risk, and then put feasible controls in place. A hierarchy of controls allows a project to establish a systematic method to minimize risk. The hierarchy of controls starts with elimination, extends to substitution and engineering controls, following to administrative controls, and finally allows for personal protective equipment when all other controls are either not feasible or "in-the-works." Strong safety cultures use standard systems to accomplish their safety goals.

Controls provide stability, and they answer questions before someone has a chance to ask. When I worked with Fluor (construction and engineering firm), we had to develop controls for every project before the job started. We had mega-projects with thousands of people on site, and we had small maintenance jobs with ten people on site. The size of the project did not matter.

We had to develop a strategic safety plan to address the specific risk associated with the work. A typical strategic safety plan would include regulatory OSHA programs, training strategies, mobilization plans, organization charts, roles and responsibilities, client requirements, applicable safety rules, and general information that the team needed to know to prevent injuries. The goal was to answer questions that you knew would arise throughout the course of the project. The best plans produced the best results.

I want to help you put your strategic plan together. In Principle 5, readers will learn five practices that demonstrate how to put prevention and control measures in place. Keep one thing in mind: you can have great policies, procedures, and rules, but if you do not enforce them, they are useless. The goal is to provide examples for how you can make your controls effective. The focus is on policies, procedures, rules, contractor safety, and corrective action. These elements anchor practices in place with documentation. If a process is on paper, you have a system to govern. Your mission is to evaluate how well your company implements the practices. Look for areas where you can improve, and put a plan in place to make it happen. With the right character, mentality, and results focus, you will make a difference!

Practice #1: The Power of Structure - The Strategic Safety Plan

I love football season. Stadium lights and fresh cut grass in the fall make me think about football. Growing up, my friends and I participated in organized leagues, and we also played in the backyard. The venue did not matter. Our competitive nature was evident in both settings. However, there were differences between a backyard game and a Friday night high school game. They required different levels of dedication and commitment.

When we played a "friendly" game of football in the backyard, we maintained the core philosophy of the game, but our adherence to the rules was liberal. The games were unregulated, and it was primarily the survival of the fittest. The backyard games lacked the structure and discipline that organized football requires.

Structure and discipline in organized sports taught me the finer points of the game. Coaches molded my personality. Rules taught me to appreciate fair competition. Dedication to practice enabled my success, and allowed teamwork to be molded into my character. All of these elements helped me learn to value the game and experience the rewards of my hard work. In essence, the structure of organized football created an environment with character, commitment, and dedication, along with a culture of clear expectations for the team.

Many companies approach safety like a backyard game, where they make up the rules as they go. These companies might have a competitive spirit, but there is no discipline to the program that drives success. They lack teamwork, direction, and boundaries for their program. The "backyard" safety culture does not experience the value of true dedication and hard work. However, companies can improve their own safety cultures if they recognize the difference and transition their organization to a structured team with focus and direction.

Companies with structure and discipline in their safety culture have the ability to teach employees the finer points of safety, just like organized sports. The structure molds the culture; mentors teach the value of safety and the rules help the employees appreciate safety success. Commitment enables achievement, but commitment also relies on teamwork. In essence, a structured and disciplined safety program creates an evolving tradition, and a culture with clear expectations for managers and employees.

What does a structured and disciplined program look like? Successful safety cultures find a way to put fundamental safety principles into practice. These companies believe a management commitment is important, and employee involvement is essential. Professionals recognize how important it is to analyze work, put controls in place, and train their employees. But the principles are only half the story. Leaders have to know how they will tactically put these principles into practice.

Just like organized sports, you have to have a game plan and strategy that puts principle to practice. The Strategic Safety Plan should include the following:

1.0 Management Commitment and Visibility
Safety commitment does not exist without a strong and consistent management presence in the workplace. The goal for this plan is to define clear ways that the management team and supervisors can demonstrate their commitment with strategic visible action. The following management **Safe Habits** will produce **Safe Work** and positive safety results.

1.1 Daily Preshift Meetings – Each area conducts a preshift meeting and safety is at the top of the agenda. These meetings are a strategic opportunity for a Project Manager and the Staff to be visible in the safety discussion.
Goal: 100% management engagement. The Project Manager and Staff should monitor the quality of the safety discussion in the meetings, and they should provide input for how to make the topics proactive and effective.

2.0 Weekly Safety Audits – The audit strategy should focus on consistent participation, frequent walkthroughs, fundamental coaching, standard protocols, consistent follow-through with corrective action, and performance-minded accountability with results.
Goal: 100% accountability for the results. The Project

Manager and Staff will participate in the weekly audits and drive the process. The audit is a strategic opportunity to demonstrate high expectations for results. "Repeat" audit items should carry consequences.

2.1   **Incident Analysis** – The Project Manager and Staff will continue to be highly engaged in the incident investigation process. For recordable accidents or severe near misses, they will participate in interviews and area walk-throughs to insure results identify all root causes.
Goal: Influence the future. Elevate visibility by participating in the details of the process. Follow through with corrective action is also a critical area of focus.

2.2   **Corrective Action** – Establish a process to track all open items for incidents. Assign target dates, responsibility, and monitoring expectations.
Goal: Drive sustainable solutions. The Project Manager and Staff should meet at least monthly to discuss corrective action follow-through. They will also evaluate how well corrective action measures were implemented and sustained plant-wide.

2.3   **Improvement Initiatives** – Safety progress requires focus on the trends. The Steering Team can provide support and direction for safety committees and managers to systematically address trends with communications, training, auditing, and engineering controls.
Goal: Solve specific problems that impact performance. The goal is to focus on the problems and generate sustainable solutions.

3.0 Employee Involvement

3.1 Hazard Identification – Employees need a clear method for identifying and correcting hazards. The Hazard Identification process is not just about creating a list of things for maintenance to do. The process should encourage employees to take action and correct the things that they control. The process should be visible and simple.

Goal: Find and fix it. Develop a Hazard Identification process that focuses on what employees can control. Use the process as a way to coach and mentor employees to look for and correct risk.

3.2 Safety Teams – The safety teams should report through a formal structure. Establish a Safety Steering Team that manages the different Safety Committees. The goal for the SST is to direct, monitor, and support the Safety Committee structure. ALL team activities should focus on safety performance improvement. They should create a strategy that includes a list of prioritized projects.

Goal: 100% employee engagement. Develop a structured Safety Team organization that meets consistently and addresses safety performance problems strategically. Get employees involved with the solutions.

3.3 Approaching Others – ALL employees need to feel comfortable approaching others about safety hazards. This skill is one of the most important elements that a program can have. Once people actively help each other in the area of safety, performance begins to improve.

Goal: Protect each other. Develop a 12-month strategy for how to promote the Approaching Others idea. The strategy should include training, communications, and consistent face-to-face promotion.

3.4 Audit Participation – Utilize audits as an opportunity to coach and mentor employees. Audit participation is also an opportunity for employees to show you where the problems are. Use audits to identify risk but also promote teamwork.
Goal: Coach and mentor employees. Conduct audits with teams including management and employees. Utilize the strengths of the entire organization.

3.5 Mentoring Program – Employees are most at risk when they are first hired. New hires are also more likely to ask a fellow employee a question. A good mentoring program identifies natural leaders in the workforce and trains them to be safety advocates. As the "mentor," these leaders have an opportunity to help new employees learn to work safely.
Goal: Empower natural leaders to make an impact on new employees. Develop a Safety Mentoring Program that identifies natural leaders and equips them to coach new employees about safety. The program should include ways to make the process highly visible. There should also be a process for evaluating new employees based on standard safety expectations.

4.0 Worksite Analysis

4.1 Audits – If the site currently has multiple methods for auditing work, then there is an opportunity to look at all methods and streamline them into an effective overall process. The safety audit strategy should focus on consistent participation, frequent walk-throughs, fundamental coaching, standard protocols, consistent follow through with corrective action, and performance-minded accountability with results. **Goal: Audit things that impact compliance and performance.** The Project Manager and Staff will participate in the weekly audits and drive the process. All layers of the organization should participate.

4.2 **Incident Investigations** – Every incident investigation should focus on how to influence the future and focus LESS on how to punish the past. A good investigation program identifies root causes, and it provides recommendations for eliminating the hazards. Good investigators have root cause training, and they utilize the skill often. **Goal: Equip people with the tools to do good investigations.** Ensure that the team is investigating near misses and recordable accidents.

4.3 **Pretask Planning** – One of the most effective ways to prevent accidents is to teach people to anticipate the risk. Good pretask planning requires employees to think through the steps of a job, identify potential injuries, and put preventive measures in place. **Goal: Get employees to think "What if?"** Develop and implement a formal Pretask Planning process. The initial process will focus on maintenance-related work and projects.

4.4 **Equipment Inspections** – Safe habits include requirements for employees to inspect the tools and equipment they use. The process should be consistent and frequent. **Goal: 100% compliance with audits.** Audit all processes that require employees to inspect equipment: manufacturing equipment, cord and plug equipment, rigging equipment, ladders, cranes/hoist, electrical PPE, forklifts, and fire extinguishers. The goal is to insure employees take this process seriously.

4.5 Analyze Trends (Audits and Injuries) – Treat safety trends just like you would a quality trend. Once you know certain things happen more frequently, determine why and put a plan in place to correct it. Utilize all available tools to train, communicate, and monitor results.
Goal: Reverse the trends.

5.0 Training and Communication

5.1 New Hire Orientations – This is the only opportunity that you get to make a first impression. The process should deliver information that covers regulatory requirements, and it also should provide relevant safety information. The delivery method should include instructor-led elements as well as video support. Participants should also take a comprehension test.
Goal: Make a positive safety impression. Have senior leaders express their commitment to safety in the orientations. Give tours if possible, and make sure employees know the basic safety *requirements.*

5.2 Regulatory Training – Maintain an annual regulatory training schedule that includes all required OSHA training. The delivery method should include instructor- led elements as well as video support. Participants should also take a comprehension test. When possible, utilize subject matter experts for the training and/or a safety professional. If that is not possible, conduct "train the trainer" sessions with the employees who will conduct the training.

Goal: Deliver good material effectively. Employees need to comprehend the topics so that they can apply the principles.

5.3 **Safety Leadership Training** (SLT) – Great programs equip all levels of the organization to perform day-to-day safety related tasks. Safety Leadership training should teach Department Managers, Coordinators, and Team Leaders topics such as (but not limited to): Why Safety is Important, Safety Responsibilities, Preplanning Techniques, Hazard Identification, Communication Skills, and Root Cause Analysis.

Goal: Teach leaders how to make a huge impact on safety. Establish a schedule and agenda for conducting SLT consistently throughout the year. Anyone who directs employees should go through the training.

5.4 **Weekly Safety Topics** – Team Leaders should deliver relevant weekly topics. Employees should apply the principles of the weekly topics in their work areas. Team Leaders should document employee participation.

Goal: Constantly communicate a relevant safety message. Managers and Coordinators should be visible in the process, and Team Leaders should encourage feedback in the meetings.

5.5 **Strategic Safety Communications** – A Safety Communications Plan should consider methods for promoting messages verbally, in writing, and visually. The plan should focus on safety performance-related topics and plant safety expectations.

Goal: Employees should see and hear a safety

message everywhere they turn. Develop a plan that keeps safety fun, but focuses on key initiatives and performance.

6.0   Prevention and Controls

6.1   Strategic Safety Plan – A Strategic Safety Plan defines how and what you want to do improve safety performance. The plan should include Safe Habits that produce Safe Work. The plan should also provide quantitative ways to measure performance.
Goal: Plan your success. To experience PEAK Safety Performance, you have to identify the path you will take and drive progress. The plan should be on paper and should be easy to track.

6.2   Rules and Programs – OSHA requires companies to have specific programs and rules in place. Employees should know what they are, and the rules should be enforced consistently. Compliance with programs and rules are a measuring stick for safety commitment.
Goal: Follow and enforce the rules relentlessly. Evaluate current "Absolutes" and determine if they are aligned with the direction your company wants to take. Make appropriate changes and create an "Absolute Pathway" for compliance to the rules.

6.3   Corrective Action Programs - Establish a process to track all open items for incidents. Assign target dates, responsibility, and monitoring expectations.
Goal: Eliminate the issue. The Project Manager and the Staff should meet at least monthly to discuss corrective action follow-through. They will also evaluate how well corrective action measures were implemented and sustained plant-wide.

6.4 Case Management – When an injury happens at work, it is extremely important for the team to stay involved with the treatment for the employee. The team should take a "hands-on" approach to the process to ensure the employee is taken care of properly.
Goal: Ensure appropriate treatment.

6.5 Annual Review – There are a lot of pieces to the safety puzzle. Each year, your team should perform an annual review to ensure that they are following all regulatory and corporate requirements. The process should also score leadership SAFE HABITS – SAFE WORK.
Goal: Recalibrate and identify areas of improvement.

Putting safety principles to practice represents the structure and discipline required to succeed. This action is how an organization demonstrates their commitment to safety. A structured plan establishes a positive culture with shared attitudes, values, goals, and practices that characterize a company's reputation. The applied principles are the difference between a backyard ballgame and an organized team. Every employee has the obligation to understand these principles and make them highly visible throughout the organization. Cultures rely on the collective influence of every individual to support the team.

I challenge you to champion the cause in your work environment. Your commitment to your culture today influences tomorrow's results! [7]

---

7. *PSJ Professional Safety*, March 2019, assp.org

Practice #2: Regulatory Programs - The OSHA Influence

Bring clarity and discipline to your culture with fundamental policies and procedures. You can only realize the full benefit of your policies and procedures when you take them off the shelf, dust them off, evaluate them, communicate them, train your staff on them, and enforce them.

Policies and procedures satisfy the requirement for "written programs" in regulations such as confined space entry, lockout tagout, hazard communication, lead work, and respiratory protection. These **written procedures** provide the requirements that are consistent with those in the OSHA regulations that workers must follow in order to be in compliance with the regulations. Still other procedures are written that help protect employees from hazards associated with common activities (not otherwise covered by regulation or industry standard), such as first line breaks, hot tapping, welding/cutting/burning, and heat stress prevention. Managers cannot expect employees to know how to behave if there are no written programs and procedures to help them. Procedures help to establish discipline and order in the safety program.

How do all of the policies and procedures fit together to form a cohesive safety program?

Do you like to put puzzles together? I don't mean the wooden puzzles that small children recognize, eat, destroy, or even flush down the toilet. I mean the big 1,000-piece puzzles with complicated colors and shapes that are difficult to match. The process can be painful to watch. To put the puzzle together, you start with the corner pieces because they are easy to recognize. Then you collect and connect all the edges of the puzzle. You use trial and error to construct the rest of the puzzle as you put the exact pieces where they belong. There are no duplicate pieces, and you reach the end of the puzzle when you put the last piece in place. One missing piece will leave you unsatisfied. You start with assorted pieces of colored cardboard, and end up with a unique masterpiece complimented by the contribution of each individual piece.

Every regulatory program and site-specific process represents one element – one piece of the puzzle – that has to fit into the overall picture. You start with your cornerstone programs that are easy to recognize and implement, such as hazard communication, confined spaces, personal protective equipment, and lockout tagout. These cornerstone programs (that is, corner pieces of your puzzle) build a firm foundation that allows you to complete the edges of your program with processes that define your culture. Once you have identified the pieces of your puzzle – the policies and procedures that will make up your program – you will need to understand the impact of the programs, and communicate roles and responsibilities to your organization. After you develop the policies and procedures, you can begin to train, monitor, and coach employees to help them understand the policies and procedures. Then you put the policies and procedures into practice (implementation).

Each policy and procedure offers a unique benefit that represents a piece of the puzzle. Your ability to lead with consistency, discipline, and clarity will establish a culture that embraces the policies and procedures that prevent injuries.

Practice #3: Critical Site Rules - Provide Focus!

"Foul ball!" "Safe!" "You're out of there!" When an umpire waves his arms and yells those words, fans see the impact of the rules with good and bad calls. Every call prompts an emotional response, and the application of the rule is visible. Good umpires are knowledgeable, observant, and consistent. They make hard calls regardless of public opinion.

During one baseball season, my son Jacob hit a beautiful line drive into right center field, beyond the reach of the outfielders. The score of the game was tight, and every run counted. With the fans cheering, Jacob rounded all the bases and headed for home. The dugout erupted as Jacob passed home plate, with what appeared to be an "in-the-park" home run. Jacob's team swarmed him after he ran back to the dugout. Then the catcher from the other team casually walked up to Jacob and touched him with the ball. The umpire screamed, "You're OUT!" The stands erupted again with a different emotion: contempt! According to the umpire, Jacob did not touch home plate. It was a stand up, uncontested, in-the-park, home run – no question about it. But Jacob missed the plate, and the rules said he was out. How was that fair?

The rules decide what is fair! No matter how bad it hurts, you have to play by the rules. Jacob learned a lesson that he will never forget. You have to tag all of the bases if you want your run to count.

Safety rules are similar. Good leaders are knowledgeable, observant, and consistent in the application of rules. Good leaders make hard calls regardless of public opinion. Focus on the simple rules teaches employees to tag all of their bases if they want to work safely.

Compliance with the rules instills discipline into program implementation, and it demonstrates your commitment to safety. Rules have to have clarity. You cannot implement rules with ambiguity and expect success. Establish simple rules with clear consequences. As a leader, make the hard calls and live with the outcome. If you do not clarify and enforce the rules with consistency, you create apathy among your employees. When you enforce the rules – and administer the consequences – you set the expectations for the future. Employees recognize the limits and they learn from your decisive choices. Rules provide a way to measure individual commitment. In time, your safety culture will improve simply because "the rules" will become second nature; and all will "know" that ignoring a rule just isn't done in your shop. Or if it is, there will be consequences!

As one measure of your safety culture, how would you rate your company's commitment to safety? Every organization should establish feasible site-specific rules to which employees must comply. Train employees on the rules and verify that they understand. Strong safety cultures have employees who know the rules, and employees have a disciplined approach to compliance with the rules. There is little confusion about right and wrong. The expectations are clear, and the consequences are appropriate and just.

Practice #4: Contractor Safety - The Agent for the Client

When I worked at Duracell, we went through an aggressive growth phase. I was the sole Safety Engineer at our plant where we manufactured AA and AAA batteries for North America and the battery business was good. We operated seven days a week, twenty-four hours a day, and we still could not keep up with the demand. The strength of the battery market led to a massive expansion of our plant. At the height of the expansion, we continued to make batteries at a record pace, even though we had construction activities on three out of the four sides of the plant. Imagine the potential hazards with construction activities in full swing while you still make a product. There was plenty of excitement and more than enough to do. I struggled to keep up with the demand.

I faced huge challenges that consumed every minute of my day, and I lost sleep over the risk involved with an operational plant working beside a large construction site. The *potential* risk was the loss of life, regulatory non-compliance, liability issues, disruptions, execution problems, and the overall public relations of the job. As I think back on that growth period, I realize how much I needed help with the construction side of my responsibilities. I was swamped with normal plant issues, and I was overwhelmed with the dynamic nature of construction.

I needed an "Agent for the Client" who could help administer three critical phases of contractor management. The construction phase was temporary, and I could have used a third-party safety professional to help get my arms around the construction activity. An Agent for the Client is someone who can act on the behalf of the client and assist with the governance of the project.

The Agent for the Client can help lead critical processes such as:

1. **Initial Contractor Safety Qualifications.** If you award work to contractors with a questionable safety record, you put your company at risk. Past history is a good indicator of future performance. Based on that principle, it is imperative that companies have a robust safety prequalification process for contractors. Review each contractor's safety performance and measure them by your standards. Disqualify contractors who do not meet your expectations.

2. **Contractor Safety Alignment.** Do not assume contractors understand your safety culture and expectations. Provide contractors with all of the appropriate rules, procedures, and policies. You can even provide sample tools such as a Principle to Practice Safety Execution Plan book. Do anything you can to help set the contractor up for success. Then meet with them face-to-face so that you can review your expectations. This is an opportunity to establish a working relationship, and clarify any confusion. When clients do not align with contractors, you will hear contractors make comments such as, "If I had known that was what you meant, I would have bid the job differently!" Alignment helps everyone know what you mean, and you should be sure to document the process to avoid future selective memory.

3. **Contractor Safety Performance Measurement and Monitoring.** You cannot improve what you do not measure. One of the top three ways to have a positive impact on safety is to audit your processes and score the performance. You can provide simple tools like the Principle to Practice Safety Walkthrough Guide to help monitor compliance with regulations. The principle also helps a client coach contractors who perform work on their property. If you measure contractor safety performance with a consistent scorecard, the process serves as an extenuation of the alignment phase. Scored audits provide a "hands-on" approach that will show contractors what the client expects. Companies should track progress and hold the contractor management team responsible for improvement.

These critical phases apply to both large and small projects, and they take time and commitment. A third-party Agent for the Client can help bridge the gap between your normal safety responsibilities and construction activity on an active plant site.

PEAK Safety Performance can serve as your "Agent for the Client." They staff professionals who lead processes for contractor selection, alignment, and monitoring. PEAK Safety representatives can audit, train, and consult clients on their contracting safety struggles. They share your burden and minimize your stress.

Do not let construction activities distract you. Great companies know how to manufacture exceptional products in a safe work environment. Success takes focus and commitment. Do not let the dynamic nature of a capital project distract you from your mission to make a product without injuring your workforce. You can achieve success in both environments if you plan for success. Incorporate a Safety Agent into your expansion budget, and let them facilitate the qualification, alignment, and monitoring phases of the job. The Agent can bridge the gap between your normal safety responsibilities and construction activity, so that you can sleep better at night.

Practice #5 – Evaluate Controls & Improve

Annual self-assessments are critical to continuous improvement. What is a self-assessment? It is a systematic, documented, and objective review of the controls that you have in place. The focus is on your management system (your policies and procedures) and regulatory requirements. A self-assessment measures effectiveness with field execution as well as administrative requirements. Self-assessments are system tools, and the process encourages sites to evaluate administrative controls. Self-assessments establish consistency and offer an opportunity for employees to learn the management system and controls in depth.

Growing up, our family had built-in health care – my mother was a nurse. My brother and I experienced a full range of sicknesses and injuries, but Mom could handle anything. If we were sick, she knew what medicine to give us. If we were hurt, she gave us a bandaid. An unplanned doctor's visit meant there was a serious problem because Mom could diagnose and treat most problems.

Even though unplanned doctor's visits were rare, my brother and I knew that we still had to suffer through an annual physical at the pediatrician. I never understood why Mom would not take us to the doctor when we were sick but without fail, she would take us for that annual physical when we felt fine! How does that make sense?

I guess if you are sick, the symptoms are obvious and the treatment is standard. Why go to the doctor just so they can tell you, "You are sick. Take two aspirin and call me in the morning." Mom could do that without getting out the checkbook. An annual physical is different. The doctor would poke and prod to look for the hidden problems. Your blood work and various samples reveal internal conditions. The annual physical looks beyond superficial signs.

The difference between site audits and self-assessments is similar to treatment for minor aches and pains versus a comprehensive checkup. A site audit requires you to walk through an area and make observations during a specific time. If you don't see anything, all is well. A comprehensive self-assessment requires that you assess and verify elements of your management system and controls. You take procedures and evaluate their effectiveness, and then you take the procedure to the field to verify that people follow the procedure. A systematic approach to checks and balances within your system will gauge the internal health of your program. The assessment and verification process is like blood work at the doctor – it reveals the hidden dangers.

Principle 5 Summary – Injury Prevention and Control

Your goal is to prevent hazards and control risk. Procedures, policies, rules, and plans help you accomplish this goal. Preventing hazards and controlling risk is like a drive in the fog. One morning I found myself navigating the fog as I drove to work. I could not see anything around me, so I used extra caution, slowed down, and took my time. I even considered not taking my usual shortcut through the country, because I was unsure what I might encounter in the fog.

Then I had a strange revelation. I thought about how it is odd that you can always see just far enough ahead of you to proceed without problems. Limited visibility slows you down, but you still get to your destination because you take the time to focus on what is directly in your path. You adjust to your environment. You put controls in place, such as a safe speed and a heightened awareness, to keep you safe.

Driving on a clear day is different. You see stop signs, red lights, crossroads, and cars in the distance, and you can prepare for them with advanced notice. You are not restricted by limited visibility, and you can make decisions easier. Your obstacles and detours are in plain sight.

Safety is very similar to traveling in the fog. There are times when you have to proceed with extreme caution due to complex circumstances. Like traveling on a clear day, there are times when you have ample warning to react to your changing environment. With both circumstances, you can still reach your destination if you approach the situation with the proper planning and controls in place.

Know your risk and adjust your plans based on that risk. In Principle 5, readers learned five practices that demonstrate how to make your controls effective. A good plan, discipline to the process, rules, and structure will build your culture. With the right character, mentality, and results in focus, you will make a difference!

Conclusion

What separates the good from the great in safety? Companies that excel in safety performance share a common characteristic. They are performance-minded and character-driven, and they demonstrate these qualities in a structured framework. Five principles anchor the framework:

1. Training and Communication
2. Management Commitment and Engagement
3. Employee Involvement and Ownership
4. Worksite Analysis
5. Hazard Prevention and Control

On a conceptual level, the principles are self-explanatory and logical. But in practice, how do employers translate the concept into meaningful performance? They demonstrate the right character, mentality, and results through structured practices.

Management Commitment and Engagement

Management commitment is the first step to building a performance-minded, character-driven safety culture. Disciplined commitment enables an organization to make difficult choices that impact safety performance. To take the first step, Top Management (in fact all leaders) must understand that commitment does not exist unless it is visible and consistent. Actions are a reflection of what people believe about achieving zero injuries. Organizations can institute techniques that enable visibility and commitment.

Practice #1: Corrective Action
Practice #2: Strategic Visibility

Practice #3: PEAK Safety Engagement
Practice #4: Participation in Event Analysis
Practice #5: Measured Accountability

Employee Involvement & Ownership

Are employees just a number? People want to work for employers who see them as individuals, and not just as statistics. Employees want to spend their eight hours-a-day with coworkers who care. Safety metrics are always important, but to build a safety way of life, ask this, "How do I visibly put people first? Am I building mutual respect?" When the focus shifts from a number to a person, safety initiatives take on a more personal focus. Going personal encourages people to take ownership of safety. Sincere ownership and involvement will promote safety success.

Practice #1: Find and Fix It
Practice #2: Hands on Safety Champions
Practice #3: Create a Mentoring Program
Practice #4: Approaching Others
Practice #5: Help with Safety Audits

Worksite Analysis

Analysis and measurement drive improvement. Companies cannot blindly achieve positive results with safety. Evaluate multiple levels of the program on a continuous basis to ensure adequate protection for employees. Thorough analysis tools allow teams to focus attention on areas that count. The main goal is to create a strategic analysis plan that identifies and addresses risk before an injury occurs. Measurement of implementation and compliance will help focus resources and attention in areas of need, as well as highlight those areas where recognition is warranted.

Practice #1: Safety Audits
Practice #2: CONTEXT Root Cause Analysis
Practice #3: Pretask Planning
Practice #4: Equipment Inspections
Practice #5: Trend Analysis

Safety and Health Training

An effective safety and health training plan has three layers: classroom training, coaching in the field, and general awareness communication. To achieve success in all three levels, organizations must equip leaders with the knowledge and the purpose of executing a meaningful training strategy. Value-added education goes beyond teaching an individual's specific skills to perform a job. Meaningful training teaches people to think about what could happen. Leaders must dedicate time to training, and they should have support systems to follow-up with positive reinforcement. A strategic training plan will include a variety of consistent and interesting safety messages.

Practice #1: First Impression Orientations
Practice #2: Regulatory Training
Practice #3: Leadership Training
Practice #4: Communicate Like a Fan
Practice #5: Safety Topics

Hazard Prevention and Control

There are almost limitless ways to prevent hazards and control risk. The key is to identify the greatest potential for risk and then put feasible controls in place. A hierarchy of controls allows a project to establish a systematic method for minimizing risk. The hierarchy of controls starts with elimination, extends to substitution and engineering controls, following to administrative controls, and finally allows for personal protective equipment when all other controls are either infeasible or "in-the-works." Strong safety cultures use standard systems for controlling risk.

> **Practice #1: The Power of Structure**
> **Practice #2: Regulatory Programs**
> **Practice #3: Critical Rules**
> **Practice #4: Contractor Safety**
> **Practice #5: Evaluate Controls and Improve**

And Finally...

There is nothing new under the sun. There is no silver bullet to achieve safety excellence. However, if you use proven principles and practices like a GPS, you can follow the blue line and **MAKE A DIFFERENCE!** There is no doubt that you may have implemented many of the ideas in this book. How do you use the ideas to develop a performance-minded, character-driven culture? You add the right safety character, mentality, and results focus to the process. The proper intentions and motivation will help an organization mature towards an injury-free culture, and the consistency of your actions will define your safety culture.